OCR

RECOGNISING ACHIEVEMENT

GCSE Mathematics

Graduated Assessment

Stages 3 & 4

Authors

Howard Baxter

Mike Handbury

John Jeskins

Jean Matthews

Mark Patmore

Contributor

Colin White

Series editor *Brian Seager*

Hodder & Stoughton

A MEMBER OF THE HODDER HEADLINE GROUP

Orders: please contact Bookpoint Ltd, 130 Milton Park, Abingdon, Oxon OX14 4SB. Telephone: (44) 01235 827720, Fax: (44) 01235 400454. Lines are open from 9.00 – 6.00, Monday to Saturday, with a 24 hour message answering service. Email address: orders@bookpoint.co.uk

British Library Cataloguing in Publication Data

A catalogue record for this title is available from The British Library.

ISBN 0 340 801891

First published 2001

Impression number 10 9 8 7 6 5 4 3 2

Year 2007 2006 2005 2004 2003 2002 2001

Cover illustration by Mike Stones.

Produced by Hardlines, Charlbury, Oxon.

Printed in Italy for Hodder & Stoughton Educational, a division of Hodder Headline Plc, 338 Euston Road, London NW1 3BH.

Acknowledgements

The Publishers would like to thank the following individuals and companies for permission to reproduce photographs in this book:

The Photographers Library: page 191

Every effort has been made to trace ownership of copyright. The Publishers would be happy to make arrangements with any copyright holder whom it has not been possible to trace.

This book covers the middle part of the specification for the Foundation tier of GCSE Mathematics. It is particularly aimed at OCR Mathematics C (Graduated Assessment) but could be used for other GCSE Mathematics examinations.

The work in this book covers the criteria in stages M3 and M4, and aims to make the best of your performance in the module tests and the terminal examination:

- Each chapter is presented in a style intended to help you understand the mathematics, with straightforward explanations and worked examples.
- At the start of each chapter is a list of what you should already know before you begin.
- There are plenty of exercises for you to work through and practise the skills.
- At the end of each chapter there is a list of key ideas.
- After every four or five chapters there is a revision exercise.
- Some exercises are designed to be done without a calculator so that you can practise for the non-calculator sections of the papers.
- Many chapters contain Activities to help you develop the necessary skills to undertake coursework.
- At frequent intervals throughout the book there are exam tips, where the experienced examiners who have written this book offer advice and tips to improve your examination performance.
- Revision exercises and Module tests are provided in the Teacher's Resource.

Part of the examination is a calculator-free zone. You will have to do the first section of each paper without a calculator and the questions are designed appropriately.

The percentage of the marks for the Assessment Objectives on the module tests and terminal examination are:

- 10% AO1 Using and Applying Mathematics
- 40% AO2 Number and Algebra
- 20% AO3 Shape, Space and Measures
- 10% AO4 Handling Data

The remaining marks to balance AO1 (10%) and AO4 (10%) are awarded to the internal assessment (coursework).

Most of the marks given for Algebra in AO2 are for 'manipulative' algebra. This includes simplifying algebraic expressions, factorising, solving equations and changing formulae. Some questions are also being set which offer you little help to get started. These are called 'unstructured' or 'multi-step' questions. Instead of the question having several parts, each of which leads to the next, you have to work out the necessary steps to find the answer. There will be examples of this kind of question in the revision tests and past examination papers.

Top ten tips

Here are some general tips from the examiners to help you do well in your tests and examination.

Practise:

1 all aspects of **manipulative algebra** in the specification
2 answering questions **without** a calculator
3 answering questions which require **explanations**
4 answering **unstructured** questions
5 **accurate** drawing and construction
6 answering questions which **need a calculator**, trying to use it efficiently
7 **checking answers**, especially for reasonable size and degree of accuracy
8 making your work **concise** and well laid out
9 using the **formula sheet** before the examination
10 **rounding** numbers, but only at the appropriate stage.

Coursework

The GCSE Mathematics examinations will assess your ability to use your mathematics on longer problems than those normally found on timed written examination papers. Assessment of this type of work will account for 20% of your final mark. It will involve two tasks, each taking about three hours. One task will be an investigation, the other a statistics task.

Each type of task has its own mark scheme in which marks are awarded in three categories or 'strands'. The titles of these strands give you clues about the important aspects of this work.

For the investigation tasks the strands are:

● Making and monitoring decisions – what you are going to do and how you will do it
● Communicating mathematically – explaining and showing exactly what you have done
● Developing the skills of mathematical reasoning – using mathematics to analyse and prove your results.

The table below gives some idea of what you will have to do and show. Look at this table whenever you are doing some extended work and try to include what it suggests you do.

Mark	Making and monitoring decisions	Communicating mathematically	Developing the skills of mathematical reasoning
1	organising work, producing information and checking results	discussing work using symbols and diagrams	finding examples that match a general statement
2	beginning to plan work, choosing your methods	giving reasons for choice of presentation of results and information	searching for a pattern using at least three results
3	finding out necessary information and checking it	showing understanding of the task by using words, symbols, diagrams	explaining reasoning and making a statement about the results found

Mark	Making and monitoring decisions	Communicating mathematically	Developing the skills of mathematical reasoning
4	simplifying the task by breaking it down into smaller stages	explaining what the words, symbols and diagrams show	testing generalisations by checking further cases
5	introducing new questions leading to a fuller solution	justifying the means of presentation	justifying solutions explaining why the results occur
6	using a range of techniques and reflecting on lines of enquiry and methods used	using symbolisation consistently	explaining generalisations and making further progress with the task
7	analysing lines of approach and giving detailed reasons for choices	using symbols and language to produce a convincing and reasoned argument	report includes mathematical justifications and explanations of the solutions to the problem
8	exploring extensively an unfamiliar context or area of mathematics and applying a range of appropriate mathematical techniques to solve a complex task	using mathematical language and symbols efficiently in presenting a concise reasoned argument	providing a mathematically rigorous justification or proof of the solution considering the conditions under which it remains valid

For the statistical tasks the strands are:

- Specifying the problem and planning – choosing or defining a problem and outlining the approach to be followed
- Collecting, processing and representing data – explaining and showing what you have done
- Interpreting and discussing results – using mathematical and statistical knowledge and techniques to analyse, evaluate and interpret your results and findings.

The marks obtained from each task are added together to give a total out of 48.

The table below gives some idea of what you will have to do and show. Look at this table whenever you are doing some extended work and try to include what it suggests you do.

Mark	Specifying the problem and planning	Collecting, processing and representing data	Interpreting and discussing results
1–2	choosing a simple problem and outlining a plan	collecting some data; presenting information, calculations and results	making comments on the data and results
3–4	choosing a problem which allows you to use simple statistics and plan the collection of data	collecting data and then processing it using appropriate calculations involving appropriate techniques; explaining what the words, symbols and diagrams show	explaining and interpreting the graphs and calculations and any patterns in the data

Mark	Specifying the problem and planning	Collecting, processing and representing data	Interpreting and discussing results
5–6	considering a more complex problem and using a range of techniques and reflecting on the method used	collecting data in a form that ensures they can be used; explaining statistical meaning through the consistent use of accurate statistics and giving a reason for the choice of presentation; explaining features selected	commenting on, justifying and explaining results and calculations; commenting on the methods used
7–8	analysing the approach and giving reasons for the methods used; using a range of appropriate statistical techniques to solve the problem	using language and statistical concepts effectively in presenting a convincing reasoned argument; using an appropriate range of diagrams to summarise the data and show how variables are related	correctly summarising and interpreting graphs and calculations and making correct and detailed inferences from the data; appreciating the significance of results obtained and, where relevant, allowing for the nature and size of the sample and any possible bias; evaluating the effectiveness of the overall strategy and recognising limitations of the work done, making suggestions for improvement

Advice

Starting a task

Ask yourself:
- what does the task tell me?
- what does it ask me?
- what can I do to get started?
- what equipment and materials do I need?

Working on the task

- Make sure you explain your method and present your results as clearly as possible
- Break the task down into stages. For example in 'How many squares on a chessboard', begin by looking at 1×1 squares then 2×2 squares, then 3×3 squares. In a task asking for the design of a container, start with cuboids then nets, surface area, prisms … Or in statistics you might want to start with a pilot survey or questionnaire.
- Write down questions that occur to you, for example, *what happens if you change the size of a rectangle systematically?* They may help you find out more about the work. In a statistical task you might wish to include different age groups or widen the type of data.

- Explore as many aspects of the task as possible.
- Develop the task into new situations and explore these thoroughly.
  - What connections are possible?
  - Is there a result to help me?
  - Is there a pattern?
  - Can the problem be changed? If so, how?

Explain your work

- Use appropriate words and suitable tables, diagrams, graphs, calculations.
- Link as much of your work together as possible, explaining, for example, why you chose the tables and charts you used and rejected others, or why the median is more appropriate than the mean in a particular statistical analysis, or why a pie chart is not appropriate. Don't just include diagrams to show identical information in different ways.
- Use algebra or symbols to give clear and efficient explanations; in investigations, you must use algebra to progress beyond about 4 marks. You will get more credit for writing $T = 5N + 1$ than for writing 'the total is five times the pattern number, plus one'.
- Don't waffle or use irrelevant mathematics; present results and conclusions clearly.

State your findings

- Show how patterns have been used and test conclusions.
- State general results in words and explain what they mean.
- Write formulae and explain how they have been found from the situations explored.
- Prove the results using efficient mathematical methods.
- Develop new results from previous work and use clear reasoning to prove conclusions.
- Make sure your reasoning is accurate and draws upon the evidence you've presented.
- Show findings in clear, relevant diagrams.
- Check you've answered the question or hypothesis.

Review/conclusion/extension

- Is the solution acceptable?
- Can the task be extended?
- What can be learned from it?

Example task

On the next page there is a short investigative task for you to try, in both 'structured' and 'unstructured' form. The structured form shows the style of a question that might appear on a timed written paper. The unstructured form represents the usual style of a coursework task. The structured form leads you to an algebraic conclusion. Notice the appearance of algebra from question 4 onwards, through a series of structured questions. These mirror the sort of questions you would be expected to think of (and answer) if you were trying it as coursework.

Comments about the questions, linking the two forms of presentation, are also shown.

Although the task in both forms directs you to investigate trapezium numbers, you would be expected to extend the investigation into other forms of number, such as pentagon numbers, to achieve the higher marks.

structured form

Trapezium numbers

These diagrams represent the first three trapezium numbers.

Each diagram always starts with two dots on the top row.

1st	2nd	3rd
2 dots	5 dots	9 dots

So the third trapezium number is 9 because nine dots can be arranged as a trapezium. There are two dots in the top row, three dots in the next row and four dots in the bottom row.

1 Write down the next two trapezium numbers

2 a) Draw a table, graph or chart of all the trapezium numbers, from the first to the tenth.
  b) Work out the eleventh trapezium number.

3 The 19th trapezium number is 209. Explain how you could work out the 20th trapezium number without drawing any diagrams.

4 Find an expression for the number of dots in the bottom row of the nth trapezium number.
Test your expression for a suitable value of n.

5 Find, giving an explanation, an expression for the number of dots in the bottom row of the diagram for the $(n + 1)$th trapezium number.

6 The nth trapezium number is x. Write down an expression in terms of x and n for the $(n + 1)$th trapezium number. Test your expression for a suitable value of n.

unstructured form

Trapezium numbers

These diagrams represent the first three trapezium numbers.

Each diagram starts with two dots on the top row.

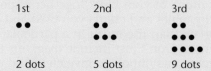

1st	2nd	3rd
2 dots	5 dots	9 dots

So the third trapezium number is 9 because nine dots can be arranged as a trapezium.

Investigate trapezium numbers

NB Although the task in this form asks you to investigate trapezium numbers, you have the freedom to – and are expected to – extend the investigation to consider other forms of number such as pentagon numbers.

Commentary

This question allows you to show understanding of the task, systematically obtaining information which **could** enable you to find an expression for trapezium numbers.

This question provides a structure, using symbols, words and diagrams, from which you should be able to derive an expression from either a table or a graph. Part **b)** could be done as a 'predict and test'.

In the unstructured form you would not normally answer a question like this.

From here you are **directed** in the structured task, and **expected** in the unstructured task, to use algebra, testing the expression – the **generalisation**.

In the unstructured form this would represent the sort of 'new' question you might ask, to lead to a further solution and to demonstrate symbolic presentation and the ability to relate the work to the physical structure, rather than doing all the analysis from a table of values.

Stage 3

CONTENTS

1 Multiplying with decimal numbers

You should already know

- how to multiply by single-digit numbers, e.g. 432×4
- that in numbers like 25·67: 2 means 2 tens, 5 means 5 units, 6 means 6 tenths and 7 means 7 hundredths.

To multiply decimal numbers by whole numbers the method is almost the same as for multiplying two whole numbers.

EXAMPLE 1

Calculate $0·3 \times 5$

Since 0·3 means $\frac{3}{10}$

Then $0·3 \times 5 = \frac{3}{10} \times 5 = \frac{15}{10} = 1·5$

This means that you can simply multiply $3 \times 5 = 15$ and then put in the decimal point.

EXAMPLE 2

Multiply $0·4 \times 7$

$4 \times 7 = 28$

so $0·4 \times 7 = 2·8$

EXAMPLE 3

Multiply $3·4 \times 6$

$$\begin{array}{r} 34 \\ \times\ 6 \\ \hline 204 \\ \hline \scriptstyle 2 \end{array} \qquad \begin{array}{r} 3·4 \\ \times\ 6 \\ \hline 20·4 \\ \hline \end{array} \qquad \text{So the answer is 20·4.}$$

ACTIVITY 1

If	What is?
$26 \times 3 = 78$	$2 \cdot 6 \times 3$
$85 \times 4 = 340$	$8 \cdot 5 \times 4$
$69 \times 9 = 621$	$6 \cdot 9 \times 9$
$34 \times 5 = 170$	$3 \cdot 4 \times 5$
$73 \times 7 = 511$	$7 \cdot 3 \times 7$

Exam tip

Notice that the number of decimal places in the question equals the number of decimal places in the answer. e.g. $3 \cdot 4 \times 6 = 20 \cdot 4$ (one decimal place in both). You will see at a later stage that this rule is still true on harder questions.

EXERCISE 1.1A

1 $0 \cdot 6 \times 3$

2 $0 \cdot 7 \times 6$

3 $0 \cdot 8 \times 7$

4 $1 \cdot 7 \times 3$

5 $7 \cdot 9 \times 8$

6 $8 \cdot 2 \times 9$

7 $9 \cdot 2 \times 4$

8 $12 \cdot 3 \times 2$

9 $17 \cdot 3 \times 5$

10 $28 \cdot 6 \times 7$

11 $323 \cdot 8 \times 2$

12 Six pieces of string are each $2 \cdot 9$ m long. What is their total length?

13 Seven leaves are each $5 \cdot 9$ cm long. What is their total length?

14 Six pieces of wood, each $23 \cdot 7$ cm long, are joined together. What is their total length?

15 Each of eight swimmers in a relay team takes $30 \cdot 7$ s to swim a length of the pool. How long will it take for the whole 8 lengths?

EXERCISE 1.1B

1 0·8 × 4
2 0·5 × 9
3 0·6 × 8
4 3·7 × 5
5 6·3 × 7
6 7·8 × 6
7 8·5 × 6
8 11·4 × 3
9 18·4 × 4

10 23·9 × 6
11 246·5 × 7
12 Four men are each 1·8 m tall. What is their total height?
13 Eight books each have a width of 6·4 cm. How much room do they take up on the bookshelf?
14 Three men each dig a section of a trench 25·7 m long. Find the total length of the trench.
15 Boxes are 40·6 cm high. How high is a stack of six boxes?

Dividing with decimal numbers

Dividing a decimal number by a whole number is also very like dividing two whole numbers.

EXAMPLE 4

Calculate   0·4 ÷ 2

0·4 is the same as $\frac{4}{10}$

Then $\frac{4}{10} \div 2 = \frac{2}{10} = 0·2$

This is the same as 4 ÷ 2, and then put in the decimal point.

EXAMPLE 5

Calculate   12·6 ÷ 3

$$\begin{array}{r} 4·2 \\ 3\overline{)12·6} \end{array}$$

Exam tip

Notice that, if you set out the division like Example 5, the decimal points stay in line.

Chapter 1   Multiplying with decimal numbers

EXERCISE 1.2A

1 $0.6 \div 3$

2 $1.5 \div 5$

3 $3.2 \div 8$

4 $7.2 \div 9$

5 $4.2 \div 3$

6 $26.5 \div 5$

7 $487.2 \div 3$

8 $201.2 \div 4$

9 Seven identical bags of potatoes weigh 38·5 kg. How much does each weigh?

10 A stack of tins is 73·8 cm high. There are six tins and each has the same height. Find the height of a tin.

EXERCISE 1.2B

1 $0.9 \div 3$

2 $1.6 \div 4$

3 $5.6 \div 7$

4 $6.3 \div 9$

5 $8.1 \div 3$

6 $36.4 \div 2$

7 $523.2 \div 8$

8 $362.4 \div 6$

9 A pile of 5 exercise books is 4·5 cm high. How thick is each book?

10 Nine identical balls have a total weight of 393.3 g. How much does each weigh?

Multiplying and dividing decimals by 10, 100, 1000, etc.

Decimals

You will need to remember how decimals are written using place value where the position of a digit gives its size.

hundreds	tens	ones	•	tenths	hundredths
4	3	5	•	2	7

4 hundreds + 3 tens + 5 ones + 2 tenths + 7 hundredths

$= 400 + 30 + 5 + \dfrac{2}{10} + \dfrac{7}{100}$

$= 435.27$

When we multiply by 10 each digit moves one column to the left:

so 35·6 × 10 = 356

hundreds	tens	ones	•	tenths	hundredths
	3	5	•	6	
×10	×10	×10			
3	5	6			

Multiplying by 100 is the same as multiplying
by 10 and then by 10 again:

so 35·6 × 100 = 3560

thousands	hundreds	tens	ones	•	tenths	hundredths
		3	5	•	6	
	×10	×10	×10			
	3	5	6			
×10	×10	×10				
3	5	6	0			

Notice that you have to put a zero in
the units column, otherwise the number
would read 356.

Dividing is a similar process but the numbers move
1 column to the right each time you divide by 10:

so that 435 ÷ 10 = 43·5

thousands	hundreds	tens	ones	•	tenths	hundredths
	4	3	5	•		
	÷10	÷10	÷10			
		4	3	•	5	

Dividing by 100 is the same as dividing by 10 and then
by 10 again, i.e. the numbers move 2 columns to the right

so 435 ÷ 100 becomes 4·35

thousands	hundreds	tens	ones	•	tenths	hundredths
	4	3	5	•		
	÷10	÷10	÷10			
		4	3	•	5	
		÷10	÷10	÷10		
			4	•	3	5

Exam tip

If you have difficulty remembering
which way to move the columns,
remember that multiplying by 10,
100, etc. must make the number
bigger. In the same way, dividing
by 10, 100, etc. must make the
number smaller.

5

Chapter 1   *Multiplying with decimal numbers*

EXAMPLE 6

Multiply 79·27 by   **a)** 10   **b)** 100   **c)** 1000

a) 79·27 × 10 = 792·7

> Move all columns to the left by one column so hundredths become tenths, tenths become ones, etc.

b) 79·27 × 100 = 7927

> Move all columns to the left by two columns.

c) 79·27 × 1000 = 79270

> Move all columns to the left by three columns. This time the hundredths become tens and so you have no ones. This means you have to insert a 0 in the ones column.

EXAMPLE 7

Divide 79·27 by   **a)** 10   **b)** 100   **c)** 1000

a) 79·27 ÷ 10 = 7·927

> Move all columns to the right by one column so hundredths become thousandths, tenths become hundredths, etc.

b) 79·27 ÷ 100 = 0·7927

> Move all columns to the right by two columns.

c) 79·27 ÷ 1000 = 0·07927

> Move all columns to the right by three columns. This time the tens become hundredths and so you have no tenths. This means you have to insert a 0 in the tenths column.

EXERCISE 1.3A

1 Multiply each of these numbers by 10.
  a) 5·6 **b)** 0·8 **c)** 7·9 **d)** 8·26 **e)** 7·34 **f)** 15·89

2 Multiply each of these numbers by 100.
  a) 5·6 **b)** 0·8 **c)** 7·9 **d)** 8·26 **e)** 7·34 **f)** 15·89

3 Multiply each of these numbers by 1000.
  a) 5·6 **b)** 0·8 **c)** 7·9 **d)** 8·26 **e)** 7·34 **f)** 15·89

4 Divide each of these figures by 10.
  a) 1·8 **b)** 2·7 **c)** 8·3 **d)** 18   **e)** 27   **f)** 483   **g)** 0·06 **h)** 7·28 **i)** 28·39

5 Divide each of these figures by 100.
  a) 1·8 **b)** 2·7 **c)** 8·3 **d)** 18   **e)** 27   **f)** 483   **g)** 0·06 **h)** 7·28 **i)** 28·39

Exercise 1.3A cont'd

6 Divide each of these figures by 1000.

    a) 1·8   **b)** 2·7   **c)** 8·3   **d)** 18   **e)** 27   **f)** 483   **g)** 0·06   **h)** 7·28   **i)** 28·39

7   15·6 × 10 000

8   17·28 × 100 000

9   956 ÷ 10 000

10 236·4 ÷ 100 000

11 A photograph is to be enlarged by a factor of 10. What will be the width of the enlargement if the width of the original is 4·6 cm?

12 A lens enlarges objects by a scale factor of 100. An object has a length of 0·2 mm. What will the length appear to be in the microscope?

13 On a model of a jumbo jet, all real lengths are divided by 100. The length of a jumbo jet is 70 m. What is the length of the model?

EXERCISE 1.3B

1 Multiply each of these numbers by 10.

    a) 8·3   **b)** 0·6   **c)** 5·9   **d)** 0.08   **e)** 9·62   **f)** 27·48

2 Multiply each of these numbers by 100.

    a) 8·3   **b)** 0·6   **c)** 5·9   **d)** 0.08   **e)** 9·62   **f)** 27·48

3 Multiply each of these numbers by 1000.

    a) 8·3   **b)** 0·6   **c)** 5·9   **d)** 0.08   **e)** 9·62   **f)** 27·48

4 Divide each of these figures by 10.

    a) 2·4   **b)** 6·1   **c)** 7·8   **d)** 51   **e)** 43   **f)** 682   **g)** 8·34   **h)** 5·07   **i)** 42·93

5 Divide each of these figures by 100.

    a) 2·4   **b)** 6·1   **c)** 7·8   **d)** 51   **e)** 43   **f)** 682   **g)** 8·34   **h)** 5·07   **i)** 42·93

6 Divide each of these figures by 1000.

    a) 2·4   **b)** 6·1   **c)** 7·8   **d)** 51   **e)** 43   **f)** 682   **g)** 8·34   **h)** 5·07   **i)** 42·93

7   0·07 × 10 000

8   48·3 × 1 000 000

Exercise 1.3B cont'd

9 7863 ÷ 10 000

10 2364 ÷ 1 000 000

11 Documents are reduced by 100 times to fit onto microfilm. What will the dimensions be of a document if the original width is 20·9 cm and the original length is 29·6 cm?

12 In 100 years earnings have multiplied on average by 1000. If someone earned £0.3 per week in 1900, what would they earn in 2000?

13 On a road map all real distances are divided by 100 000 to get the distance on the map.

    a) The distance from Longcroft to Winter Bay is 8000 m. How far is it on the map?

    b) On the map the distance from Gradbridge to Lowton Waters is 0·3 m. How far is it actually?

Key ideas

- To multiply 4·3 × 4, for example, first multiply 43 × 4 = 172 and then put in the decimal point, i.e. 17·2.
- To divide 17·2 ÷ 4, for example, first divide 172 by 4 and then put in the decimal point.
- To multiply decimals by 100, for example, move all columns two places to the left. So 23·7 × 100 = 2370.
- To multiply by 1000 move all columns three places to the left, and so on.
- To divide decimals by 100, for example, move all columns two places to the right. So 23·7 ÷ 100 = 0·237.
- To divide by 1000 move all columns three places to the right, and so on.

2 Metric and imperial measurements

You should already know

- how to add, subtract, multiply and divide whole numbers
- fraction and decimal notation
- how to multiply and divide decimals with a calculator.

Mass or weight

Strictly speaking the proper name is **mass,** but **weight** is the word commonly used.

Mass can be measured

either in imperial units – stones, pounds and ounces
or in metric units – grams and kilograms, which are written as g and kg.

The imperial units for mass are rarely used nowadays – ounces in recipes, pounds mostly for vegetables and stones for people's weights.

1 stone = 14 pounds, and 1 pound = 16 ounces (you do not need to learn these facts).

The short version for pounds is lb.

Nearly all masses are given in metric units.

To get a good idea of a kilogram, think of a bag of sugar which weighs 1 kilogram.

Small masses like the sugar on a spoon are weighed in grams but larger weights are usually given in kilograms.

You may need to change from kilograms to grams, or grams to kilograms. You should remember that

1 kilogram = 1000 grams

(just as 1 kilometre = 1000 metres).

ACTIVITY 1

You will need some scales which measure in both grams and ounces, and some tins or packets.

Weigh the tins or packets in both imperial and metric units and record these weights in a copy of this table.

Object	Imperial weight	Metric weight

If you have large (bathroom) scales you can weigh yourself too.

Work out how many grams are in an ounce and how many pounds in a kilogram.

Area, volume and capacity

The only units that you need to use for area and volume are metric units.

For small areas, like the area of a desk top, the units are cm^2, said 'centimetres squared'.

For larger areas, like the area of surface of a classroom floor, the units are m^2, said 'metres squared'.

For even larger areas, like the area of a town, the units are km^2, said 'kilometres squared'.

All you need to do with these is know when to use them.

For small volumes, like the volume of a small box, the units are cm^3, said 'centimetres cubed'. For large volumes, like the volume of a room, the units are m^3, said 'metres cubed'.

As with area, all you need to know is when to use them.

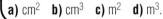

EXAMPLE 1

What units would be used for

a) the area of a page of a book   b) the volume of my brief case
c) the area of the school playground d) the volume of the school hall?

a) cm^2 b) cm^3 c) m^2 d) m^3.

When a volume is filled with liquid or gas it is called the **capacity** (or **volume**).

The imperial (old) units that you may still need are pints and gallons.

Pints are used for milk and beer. Gallons are hardly used now.

The metric units used are millilitres (written ml), centilitres (written cl), and litres (written l).

A millilitre is exactly the same as a cm^3, but is used for liquids rather than cm^3.

Millilitres are used for small amounts like the amount in a teaspoon.

Centilitres are used for the capacity of cans or small bottles of drink, although sometimes millilitres are used instead.

33 cl or 330 ml

Litres are now used for petrol and also for bottles of fizzy drinks and sometimes milk.

As with lengths

    1000 ml = 1l,
    100 cl = 1l,
    and 10 ml = 1 cl.

11

ACTIVITY 2

You need a measuring cylinder or jug and some containers such as a cup, jug, milk bottle and basin. Fill the containers with water and then pour the water into the measuring jug or cylinder and measure the capacity.

Record the results in a copy of the table.

Container	Capacity

If you used a milk bottle, how many millilitres are there in a pint?

EXAMPLE 2

a) Change these to millilitres.

    (i) 14 cl   **(ii)** 2·5 cl   **(iii)** 5 l   **(iv)** 5·23 l

b) Change these to litres.

    (i) 400 cl   **(ii)** 1250 ml   **(iii)** 5240 cl   **(iv)** 813 ml

a) **(i)** $14 \times 10 = 140\,ml$ **Multiply by 10 to change cl to ml.**

    (ii) $2·5 \times 10 = 25\,ml$

    (iii) $5 \times 1000 = 5000\,ml$ **Multiply by 1000 to change l to ml.**

    (iv) $5·23 \times 1000 = 5230\,ml$

b) **(i)** $400 \div 100 = 4\,l$ **Divide by 100 to change cl to l.**

    (ii) $1250 \div 1000 = 1·25\,l$ **Divide by 1000 to change ml to l.**

    (ii) $5240 \div 100 = 52·4\,l$

    (iv) $813 \div 1000 = 0·813\,l$

EXERCISE 2.1A

1 In what imperial (old) units would you give the mass of

    a) a penny   **b)** a bag of potatoes   **c)** a small chocolate bar   **d)** a pig?

2 In what metric units would you give the mass of

    a) a penny   **b)** a bag of potatoes   **c)** a small chocolate bar   **d)** a pig?

Exercise 2.1A cont'd

3 What metric units would you use to give
   a) the area of a photograph   **b)** the volume of a box of pencils
   c) the area of a field   **d)** the volume of a tent   **e)** the area of London?

4 In what metric units would you give the capacity of
   a) a cup   **b)** a bath   **c)** a swimming pool   **d)** a bottle of cough mixture?

5 Change these capacities to millilitres
   a) 4 l   **b)** 5·22 l   **c)** 9·16 l   **d)** 8·2 cl   **e)** 52 cl.

6 Change these capacities to litres
   a) 30 000 ml   **b)** 5234 ml   **c)** 464 cl   **d)** 1245 cl   **e)** 9503 cl.

7 Write these capacities in order of size, smallest first.
   2·42 l, 1623 ml, 84 cl, 9·044 l, 51·04 cl.

EXERCISE 2.1B

1 In which imperial (old) units would you give the mass of
   a) a bucket of sand   **b)** a tablespoon of sugar   **c)** 1 apple   **d)** a full suitcase?

2 In what metric units would you give the mass of
   a) a bucket of sand   **b)** a tablespoon of sugar   **c)** 1 apple   **d)** a full suitcase?

3 What metric units would you use to give
   a) the area of an envelope   **b)** the volume of a wardrobe
   c) the area of the deck of a ship   **d)** the volume of the boot of a car
   e) the area of a football pitch?

4 In what metric units would you give the capacity of
   a) a sauce bottle   **b)** a bucket   **c)** a petrol tank   **d)** a yoghurt carton?

5 Change these capacities to millilitres
   a) 7 l   **b)** 1·52 l   **c)** 0·16 l   **d)** 8·02 cl   **e)** 41 cl.

6 Change these capacities to litres
   a) 2000 ml   **b)** 2341 ml   **c)** 4642 cl   **d)** 245 cl   **e)** 35·2 cl.

7 Write these capacities in order of size, smallest first
   3·12 l, 1593 ml, 184 cl, 1·044 l, 51·04 ml.

Chapter 2   *Metric and imperial measurements*

Equivalent imperial (old) units and metric units

You need to know the following

1 km is about $\frac{5}{8}$ mile	8 km is about 5 miles
1 m = 39·37 inches	1 m is about 40 inches
1 foot = 30·5 cm	1 foot is about 30 cm
1 inch = 2·54 cm	1 inch is about 2·5 cm or 25 mm
1 kg = 2·2 lb	1 kg is about 2 lb
1 litre is about $1\frac{3}{4}$ pints	4 litres is about 7 pints
1 gallon is about 4·5 litres	1 gallon is about $4\frac{1}{2}$ litres

You only need to find the approximate or rough equivalents, so just use the approximate connections.

EXAMPLE 3

Change these measures in imperial units to the rough equivalents in metric units.

a) 15 miles **b)** 12 lb **c)** 5 feet **d)** 5 pints

a) 15 miles = 15 × 8 ÷ 5 = 24 km

> **8 km = 5 miles, so to change from miles to kilograms, multiply by 8 and divide by 5.**

b) 12 lb = 12 ÷ 2 = 6 kg

> **1 kg is about 2 lb, so to change from lb to kg, divide by 2.**

c) 5 feet = 5 × 30 = 150 cm or 1·5 m

> **1 foot is about 30 cm so to change from feet to centimetres, multiply by 30, then divide by 100 to change to m.**

d) 5 pints = 5 × 4 ÷ 7 = 2·86 l
  (or roughly 2·9 or 3 l)

> **4 litres = 7 pints, so to change pints to litres, multiply by 4 and divide by 7.**

> In **d)** using a calculator gives a number of decimal places but this is only a rough change so 2·9 or 3 litres is near enough.

EXAMPLE 4

Change these measures in imperial units to the rough equivalents in metric units.

a) 20 km   **b)** 3 m   **c)** 10 l   **d)** 15 kg

a) 20 km = 20 × 5 ÷ 8 = 12·5 miles

> **8 km = 5 miles, so to change kilograms to miles, multiply by 5 and divide by 8.**

b) 3 m = 3 × 40 = 120 inches = 10 feet

> **1 m = about 40 inches so to change from metres to inches, multiply by 40. As there are 12 inches in a foot you can divide by 12 to give the answer in feet.**

c) 10 l = 10 × 7 ÷ 4 = 17·5 pints

> **4 litres = 7 pints, so to change from litres to pints, multiply by 7 and divide by 4.**

d) 15 kg = 15 ÷ 2 = 7·5 lb

> **1 kg = about 2 lb so to change from kg to lb, divide by 2.**

EXERCISE 2.2A

Use a calculator if you wish but only give rough or approximate answers.

1 Change these lengths from imperial units to their rough metric equivalents.
   a) 3 feet   **b)** 8 inches   **c)** 25 miles   **d)** 150 miles.

2 Change these masses from imperial units to their rough metric equivalents.
   a) 1 lb   **b)** 16 lb   **c)** 45 lb.

3 Change these capacities from imperial units to their rough metric equivalents.
   a) 21 pints   **b)** 45 pints   **c)** 3 gallons   **d)** 10 gallons.

4 Change these lengths from metric units to their rough imperial equivalents.
   a) 15 km   **b)** 15 cm   **c)** 1·6 m   **d)** 150 km.

5 Change these masses from metric units to their rough imperial equivalents.
   a) 8 kg   **b)** 15 kg   **c)** 45 kg.

6 Change these capacities from metric units to their rough imperial equivalents.
   a) 12 litres   **b)** 45 litres   **c)** 180 litres.

Exercise 2.2A cont'd

7 John is 6 feet tall. What is his height in metres?

8 Petra bought a 10 litre can of paint.
How many pints is this?

9 Charmain was told by her mum to buy half a pound of bacon.
The shop only sells it in grams. How many grams should she buy?

10 Pearl drove 135 miles on the M1. How far is this in kilometres?

11 Joshua is 1·75 m tall. What is his height in inches?

12 In judo a 'heavyweight' weighs over 205 pounds. What is this weight in kg?

13 The distance from Nottingham to Sheffield is 72 km. How far is this in miles?

Exam tip

When changing between imperial and metric measurements, decide whether to multiply or divide the measurements by considering which is the smaller unit. A larger number of smaller units is equal to a smaller number of larger units.

EXERCISE 2.2B

Use a calculator if you wish but only give rough or approximate answers.

1 Change these lengths from imperial units to their rough metric equivalents.

   a) 15 inches   **b)** 8 feet   **c)** 125 miles   **d)** 480 miles.

2 Change these masses from imperial units to their rough metric equivalents.

   a) 10 lb   **b)** 6 lb   **c)** 53 lb.

3 Change these capacities from imperial units to their rough metric equivalents.

   a) 14 pints   **b)** 52 pints   **c)** 2 gallons   **d)** 12 gallons.

4 Change these lengths from metric units to their rough imperial equivalents.

   a) 6 m   **b)** 9 cm   **c)** 1·2 m   **d)** 450 km.

5 Change these masses from metric units to their rough imperial equivalents.

   a) 10 kg   **b)** 1·8 k   **c)** 52 kg.

6 Change these capacities from metric units to their rough imperial quivalents.

   a) 20 litres   **b)** 4·5 litres   **c)** 70 litres.

7 Sharon cycled 35 miles one Saturday.
How far is this in kilometres?

8 Conrad bought 5 pounds of potatoes. How many kilograms is this?

9 Sheila's mass is 60 kilograms.

   a) How many pounds is this?

   b) What is her mass in stones, to the nearest stone?
     (1 stone is equal to 14 pounds.)

10 This bottle holds 2 litres. How many pints is this?

Exercise 2.2B cont'd

11 Lisa fills up her car with 8 gallons of petrol. How many litres is this?

12 A road has a maximum width of 8 feet. Convert this to cm.

13 The speed limit on a road is 40 miles per hour. How many kilometres per hour is this?

Key ideas

- The imperial units still in use are:

    length: inch, foot, mile

    mass: pound, ounce, and sometimes stone

    capacity: pint, gallon.

- The metric units are:

    length: metre (m), centimetre (cm), millimetre (mm), kilometre (km)

    mass: gram (g), kilogram (kg)

    capacity: litre (l), centilitre (cl), millilitre (ml)

    area: cm^2, m^2, km^2

    volume: cm^3, m^3.

- Suitable units should be chosen remembering that

    1 m = 100 cm = 1000 mm and 1 km = 1000 m

    1 kg = 1000 g

    1 litre = 100 cl = 1000 ml.

- Imperial/metric approximate equivalents are

    8 km is about 5 miles

    1 m is about 40 inches

    1 inch is about 2·5 cm or 25 mm

    1 kg is just about over 2 lb (2·2 lb)

    4 litres is about 7 pints

    1 gallon is about $4\frac{1}{2}$ litres.

Chapter 2   *Metric and imperial measurements*

Negative numbers

You should already know

- how to add and subtract whole numbers
- how to read whole numbers off a scale.

Some numbers are less than zero. These are called negative numbers. They are written as ordinary numbers with a minus sign in front.

The minus sign tells you that the number is below zero and the number tells you how far it is below zero.

Negative numbers are used in many situations.

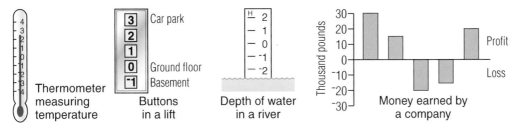

In this chapter you will be concentrating on the use of negative numbers on the temperature scale.

This is a temperature scale from ⁻10° to 10°.

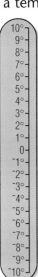

Notice that ⁻10° is lower than ⁻1°. ⁻10° is 10° below zero but ⁻1° is only 1° below zero.

Remember that zero is neither positive nor negative.

The temperature scale may help you with the next exercises. Copy it into your book. Make it longer if you wish.

ACTIVITY 1

The following table gives the average temperatures in January and July for 10 European cities.

City	January (°C)	July (°C)
Amsterdam	2	17
Athens	9	27
Berlin	⁻1	18
Bucharest	⁻3	22
Budapest	⁻1	21
Dublin	5	15
Moscow	⁻9	18
Paris	3	19
Stockholm	⁻3	18
Vienna	⁻1	19

a) Put the January temperatures on a number line.

b) Write the January temperatures in order, lowest first.

c) Work out the range of temperatures for each of the cities (for example, for Amsterdam the range is from 2 to 17).

d) Which city has **(i)** the greatest range **(ii)** the smallest range?

EXERCISE 3.1A

1 Copy and complete the following. Use the word 'warmer' or 'colder' to fill the gaps.

a) 7° is _____ than 2°   **c)** ⁻10° is _____ than 5°

b) ⁻3° is _____ than 0°   **d)** ⁻7° is _____ than ⁻12°

2 The table gives the average temperatures in January and July for five cities.

City	January (°C)	July (°C)
Casablanca	12	22
Jeddah	23	33
New York	0	25
Montreal	⁻10	21
Beijing	⁻5	31

a) Put the January temperatures on a number line.

b) Write the January temperatures in order, lowest first.

c) Work out the range of temperatures for each of the cities.

d) Which city has the greatest range?

Exercise 3.1A cont'd

3 Write these temperatures in order, lowest first.

a) ‾4°, 5°, ‾2°, 3°, ‾7°

b) ‾8°, 2°, 8°, 0°, ‾9°

c) ‾4°, ‾1°, 6°, 8°, 5°, ‾3°

d) ‾10°, 8°, ‾5°, ‾9°, 2°, ‾1°

4 Copy the table and fill in the gaps.

Start temp. (°C)	Move (°C)	Finish temp. (°C)
a) 4	Up 3	
b) ‾2	Down 4	
c) 10	Down 14	
d) ‾10		‾2
e) 10		‾9
f) ‾4		2
g)	Up 7	10
h)	Down 6	‾9
i)	Up 2	‾8
j) ‾5	Down 3	

5 Write down the next three temperatures in each of these sequences.

a) 10°, 6°, 2°, _____ , _____ , _____

b) 4°, 2°, 0°, _____ , _____ , _____

c) ‾9°, ‾6°, ‾3°, _____ , _____ , _____

d) ‾40°, ‾30°, ‾20°, _____ , _____ , _____

6 What is the difference in temperature between the following?

a) 13° and ‾5°

b) ‾10° and 15°

c) ‾20° and ‾2°

d) 25° and ‾25°

EXERCISE 3.1B

1 Copy and complete the following.
Use the word 'warmer' or 'colder' to fill the gaps.

a) 10° is .... than 0°

b) ⁻2° is .... than ⁻5°

c) 4° is .... than ⁻1°

d) ⁻2° is .... than 2°

2 Write these temperatures in order, lowest first.

a) ⁻2°, 7°, 0°, ⁻5°, 3°

b) ⁻2°, 5°, 1°, 2°, ⁻1°

c) 7°, ⁻7°, 4°, ⁻9°, ⁻3°

d) 9°, 4°, ⁻2°, 7°, ⁻8°, ⁻1°.

3 Copy the table and fill in the gaps

Start temp. (°C)	Move °(°C)	Finish temp. (°C)
a) 2	Up 7	
b) 0	Down 6	
c) ⁻6	Up 2	
d) 4		⁻7
e) ⁻6		⁻10
f) 3		⁻3
g)	Down 4	⁻7
h)	Up 3	⁻5
i)	Down 6	0
j)	Up 7	4

4 Write down the next three terms in each of these sequences.

a) 8°, 5°, 2°, ..., ..., ...

b) 2°, 1°, 0°, ..., ..., ...

c) ⁻10°, ⁻8°, ⁻6°, ..., ..., ...

d) 10°, 5°, 0°, ..., ..., ...

5 What is the difference in temperature between the following

a) 17°C and ⁻1°C   **c)** ⁻19°C and ⁻5°C

b) ⁻8°C and 12°C   **d)** 30°C and ⁻18°C?

Exercise 3.1B cont'd

Extension questions

6 The following table gives the heights above sea level, in metres, of seven places.

Place	Height (m)
Mount Everest	8863
Bottom of Lake Baykal	⁻1484
Bottom of Dead Sea	⁻792
Ben Nevis	1344
Mariana Trench	⁻11 022
Mont Blanc	4807
World's deepest cave	⁻1602

a) Put these heights in order, smallest first.

b) What is the difference in height between the highest and lowest places?

Key ideas

● **Negative numbers are less than zero. The minus sign tells you that the number is below zero and the digits tell you how far below zero.**

● **Negative and positive numbers can be represented on a numbers line like the one on the right. A number lower on the number line than another is a smaller number.**

10
9
8
7
6
5
4
3
2
1
0
-1
-2
-3
-4
-5
-6
-7
-8
-9
-10

4 Formulae

You should already know

- how to add, subtract, multiply and divide whole numbers
- fraction and decimal notation.

Formulae in words

EXAMPLE 1

To find the perimeter of a rectangle add the length and width and then multiply the total by 2. Work out the perimeter of these rectangles.

a) length = 4 cm
   width = 3 cm

b) length = 5·8 cm
   width = 3·2 cm

a) length + width = 4 + 3 = 7 cm
   Perimeter = 7 × 2 = 14 cm.

b) length + width = 5·8 + 3·2 = 9 cm
   Perimeter = 9 × 2 = 18 cm.

EXAMPLE 2

To work out the charge to hire a coach in £, Mrs Martin multiplies the number of miles by 2 and adds on 50. How much does Mrs Martin charge to hire the coach to travel

a) 100 miles

b) 225 miles?

a) 100 × 2 + 50 = 200 + 50 = £250

b) 225 × 2 + 50 = 450 + 50 = £500

EXERCISE 4.1A

1   The cost of potatoes is the cost of one kilogram multiplied by the number
    of kilograms bought. Work out the cost of 3 kilograms when 1 kilogram costs
    20 pence.

2   The time in minutes needed to cook a piece of beef is the weight of the beef
    in kilograms multiplied by 40. How many minutes are needed to cook a piece
    of beef weighing
    a) 2 kilograms   **b)** 3·5 kilograms?

3   To find Arun's age, add 6 years to Peter's age. How old is Arun if Peter is
    a) 13 years   **b)** 40 years?

4   To find the average of two numbers, add them together and then divide by 2.
    Find the average of
    a) 4 and 8   **b)** 9 and 6   **c)** 4·5 and 2·3.

5   The cost of booking a room for a meeting is £50 plus £10 per hour.
    How much does it cost to book a room for
    a) 3 hours   **b)** 12 hours?

6   The speed of a car in miles per hour
    is found from the distance travelled in
    miles divided by the time taken in hours.
    Find the speed of a car when
    a) distance = 75 miles, time = 3 hours
    b) distance = 94 miles, time = 4 hours.

Chapter 4   *Formulae*

Exercise 4.1A cont'd

7 To find the number of minutes it takes to type a letter, divide the number of words in the letter by the number of words typed in a minute. How many minutes does it take to type a letter when

   a) length of letter = 120 words, words typed in a minute = 30

   b) length of letter = 220 words, words typed in a minute = 40?

8 To work out what Joe earns in a week, multiply the number of hours worked by £5. How much does he get paid if he works

   a) 40 hours   **b)** 35 hours?

9 To find the volume of a pyramid, multiply the area of the base by the height and divide by 3. Work out the volume of a pyramid when the area of the base is 6 cm^2 and the height is 5 cm.

10 To change speed from metres per second to miles per hour, multiply by 9 and divide by 4.

   a) David can cycle at 8 metres per second. What is this in miles per hour?

   b) Stacey is driving a car at 32 metres per second. What is this in miles per hour?

EXERCISE 4.1B

1 The distance in metres rowed on a rowing machine is the number of strokes multiplied by 4. How far did John row when he did

   a) 55 strokes   **b)** 260 strokes?

2 The area of a parallelogram is equal to the base multiplied by the vertical height. What is the area of a parallelogram when

   a) base = 4 cm, vertical height = 3 cm

   b) base = 5·2 cm, vertical height = 3 cm?

3 The cost of an article in French francs is the cost in pounds times 11. What does an article cost in French francs if its cost in pounds is

   a) £5   **b)** £12.50?

4 The height that a person can reach up a wall from a ladder is 2·5 metres plus their own height. How far can a woman reach up a wall if her height is

   a) 1·3 m   **b)** 1·47 m?

5 The volume of a cuboid is the length multiplied by the width multiplied by the height. What is the volume of a cuboid with

   a) length = 4 cm, width = 3 cm, height = 5 cm

   b) length = 4·5 cm, width = 3 cm, height = 4 cm?

6 The charge in pounds by Berry motors for a taxi to the airport is 20 plus the number of miles travelled. How much is the charge for travelling

   a) 25 miles   **b)** 60 miles?

7 A rough rule to find the distance round the edge of a circular pond is to multiply the diameter of the pond by 3. What is the distance round a pond when the diameter is

   a) 5 m   **b)** 6·4 m?

Exercise 4.1B cont'd

8 In a sale they reduced all the prices. To work out the sale price they multiplied the normal price by 0·8. What was the sale price if the normal price was

a) £20 **b)** £25?

9 To change a distance from kilometres to miles multiply by 5 and divide by 8. Change these distances from kilometres to miles

a) 40 km **b)** 120 km.

10 An American magazine suggested that on average the number of words a child knows can be found by multiplying the child's age in months by 60 and subtracting 900.

a) How many words should a child know when it is

(i) 18 months old

(ii) 5 months old?

b) What does **(ii)** suggest about this rule?

Formulae in symbols

EXAMPLE 3

For the formula $F = 7 + 2a$, work out F when

a) $a = 3$, **b)** $a = \frac{1}{2}$

a) $F = 7 + 2 \times 3 = 7 + 6 = 13$

b) $F = 7 + 2 \times \frac{1}{2} = 7 + 1 = 8$

2a means
$2 \times a$

EXAMPLE 5

The formula for the volume of a cuboid is $A = a \times b \times c$ when the sides are a, b and c in length. Find A when

a) $a = 2$, $b = 4$, $c = 6$ **b)** $a = 5·5$, $b = 2$, $c = 3$

a) $A = 2 \times 4 \times 6 = 48$ **b)** $A = 5·5 \times 2 \times 3 = 33$.

EXAMPLE 4

$T = \dfrac{3a + 2b}{10}$

Work out T when

a) $a = 6$, $b = 11$

b) $a = 4$, $b = \frac{1}{2}$

a) $T = \dfrac{3 \times 6 + 2 \times 11}{10} = \dfrac{18 + 22}{10} = \dfrac{40}{10} = 4$

b) $T = \dfrac{3 \times 4 + 2 \times \frac{1}{2}}{10} = \dfrac{13}{10} = 1·3$

EXERCISE 4.2A

1 $A = 11 + 5c$. Find A when
   a) $c = 3$ **b)** $c = \frac{1}{2}$

2 $Y = 23 - 3x$. Find Y when
   a) $x = 2$ **b)** $x = 4 \cdot 5$ **c)** $x = \frac{1}{4}$

3 $P = 7q - 3$. Find P when
   a) $q = 5$ **b)** $q = 1 \cdot 8$ **c)** $q = \frac{1}{2}$

4 $W = 5x + 3y$. Find W when
   a) $x = 4, y = 2$ **b)** $x = 3, y = 3 \cdot 1$ **c)** $x = \frac{1}{4}, y = 4$

5 $H = 4d - e$. Find H when
   a) $d = 3, e = 7$ **b)** $d = \frac{1}{2}, e = 1$ **c)** $d = 2 \cdot 8, e = 3 \cdot 6$

6 $S = p \times q \times r$. Find S when
   a) $p = 4, q = 3, r = 5$ **b)** $p = 2 \cdot 1, q = 3 \cdot 5, r = 2 \cdot 8$

7 $A = 20 - f \times g$. Find A when
   a) $f = 3, g = 5$ **b)** $f = 3 \cdot 2, g = 2 \cdot 7$

8 The cost of electricity, in pence, is given by the formula $C = 900 + 6n$
   where n is the number of units used. Find the cost in pounds, when
   a) $n = 200$ **b)** $n = 1250$.

9 The volume of a brick is given by the formula $V = l \times w \times h$ where l is the height,
   w is the width and h is the height. Find the volume of a brick when
   a) $l = 25, w = 8, h = 12$ **b)** $l = 9 \cdot 6, w = 4 \cdot 2, h = 3 \cdot 5$

10 The cost of renting a car, in pounds, is given by the formula
   $C = 15d + 0 \cdot 2\,m$
   where d is the number of days of the hire and m is the number of miles travelled.
   a) Find C when $d = 2$ and $n = 300$.
   b) Find the cost of hiring a car for 5 days and travelling 800 miles.

Exercise 4.2A cont'd

11 The exact formula for conversion from temperatures on the Celsius (*C*) scale to the Fahrenheit (*F*) scale is $F = 1\cdot8C + 32$. Estimate the temperature in Fahrenheit if it is

    a) 40 °C   **b)** 10 °C   **c)** 0 °C.

12 A car hire company uses the formula $C = 20n + 10$ to calculate the cost of hire. *C* is the total cost in £ and *n* is the number of days for which the car is hired. Calculate the cost of hiring a car for

    a) 3 days   **b)** 5 days   **c)** a fortnight.

EXERCISE 4.2B

1 $B = 25 + 4a$. Find *B* when

    a) $a = 2$ **b)** $a = \frac{1}{2}$.

2 $C = 32 - 3b$. Find *C* when

    a) $b = 2$ **b)** $b = 7$ **c)** $b = 0$.

3 $D = 8e - 1$. Find *D* when

    a) $e = 2$ **b)** $e = 1\cdot2$ **c)** $e = \frac{1}{4}$.

4 $E = 4c + 3d$. Find *E* when

    a) $c = 1, d = 0$ **b)** $c = 6, d = 2$ **c)** $c = 2\cdot1, d = 2$.

5 $F = 5p - 2q$. Find *F* when

    a) $p = 9, q = 7$ **b)** $p = 6, q = 2\cdot5$ **c)** $p = 1, q = \frac{1}{2}$.

6 $G = a \times b$. Find *G* when

    a) $a = 4, b = 2$ **b)** $a = 2, b = 2\cdot4$ **c)** $a = 8, b = \frac{1}{4}$.

7 $H = 4 + 2 \times r \times s$. Find *H* when

    a) $r = 3, s = 6$ **b)** $r = 3\cdot4, s = 5$.

8   The area of a triangle is given by the formula $A = b \times h \div 2$, when *b* is the base and *h* the vertical height. Work out the area when

    a) $b = 3, h = 6$ **b)** $b = 5, h = 3$ **c)** $b = 4, h = 1\frac{1}{2}$.

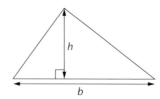

Exercise 4.2B cont'd

9 The formula for the time in hours taken for a journey is

$$t = \frac{d}{s}$$

where d is the distance in kilometres and s is the speed in kilometres per hour.
Find t when

a) $d = 160$, $s = 40$ **b)** $d = 150$, $s = 60$.

10 An approximate formula to change temperature in °C to °F is

$F = 30 + 2C$.

Use this formula to find F when C equals

a) 10   **b)** 27.

11 The time for cooking a piece of meat is given
by $T = 45W + 30$ where T is the time in
minutes and W is the weight of the meat in kg.
Find the cooking time for a piece of meat
which weighs

a) 2 kg   **b)** 1·5 kg   **c)** 5 kg.

12 The exact formula for converting from
temperature in Celsius (C) to Fahrenheit (F)
is $F = \frac{5}{9}(C - 32)$. Find the temperature in the
Celsius scale if it is

a) 77 °F   **b)** 50 °F   **c)** 32 °F.

ACTIVITY 1 – EXTENSION

Here are three sequences.

(i)   5   8   11   14   ....

(ii)   1   5   9   13   ....

(iii) 24   44   64   84   ....

In each case find the next two terms. Try to spot the
rule. Try to write the rule as a formula.

Key ideas

● In algebra if an expression says **5a**
it means $5 \times a$.

● When substituting in a formula,
work out each term separately
and then combine these amounts.

A1 Revision exercise

Do not use a calculator for the first five questions.

1 Work out

a) 0.7×9 **b)** 2.6×8
c) 7.3×7 **d)** 23.8×4
e) $3.6 \div 4$ **f)** $22.8 \div 6$.

2 A table is 1.4 m long. How long are 6 tables placed together?

3 Work out

a) 5.3×10 **b)** 6.4×100
c) 6.79×1000 **d)** $53.92 \times 10\,000$.

4 Work out

a) $5.6 \div 10$ **b)** $8.9 \div 100$
c) $23.8 \div 100$ **d)** $72.89 \div 1000$.

5 On a plan all distances are divided by 1000. A building is actually 48.6 m long. What will the length of the building be on the plan?

6 In what metric units would you measure

a) the mass of the suitcase for your holiday

b) the area of Cambridgeshire

c) the capacity of a mug?

7 Change these capacities to litres

a) 6 400 ml   **b)** 15 000 ml
c) 420 cl.

8 Change these measures in imperial units to approximate amounts in metric units.

a) 5 lb   **b)** 20 miles
c) 3 gallons   **d)** 24 feet

9 Hannah is 1.6 m tall. What is her approximate height in feet and inches?

10 Write these masses in order, smallest first.

872 g, 60 g, 4.2 kg, 5600 g, 0.793 kg

11 Arrange these temperatures in order, smallest first.

$8\,°C$, $^-3\,°C$, $0\,°C$, $5\,°C$, $^-1\,°C$, $^-6\,°C$

12 Copy these and fill in the gaps with 'higher' or 'lower'.

a) $8°$ is a .... temperature than $^-10°$

b) $^-2°$ is a .... temperature than $0°$

c) $^-5°$ is a .... temperature than $^-9°$

13 In one winter day the minimum temperature was $^-4\,°C$ and the maximum temperature was $7\,°C$. What was the difference between these temperatures?

14 The cost of a child ticket on the YTS bus is half that of an adult plus 20p.

Work out the cost of a child ticket when an adult ticket costs

a) 80p   **b)** £2.20.

15 The area of a rhombus is found by multiplying the lengths of the diagonals together and then dividing by 2. Find the area of a rhombus with diagonals

a) 4 and 6   **b)** 3 and 7
c) 2.4 and 8.

16 a) $P = 2a + 7$. Find P when
  (i) $a = 7$ **(ii)** $a = 6.5$ **(iii)** $a = \frac{1}{2}$

b) $T = 3c + 2d$. Find T when
  (i) $c = 3$ and $d = 2$
  (ii) $c = 0$ and $d = 5$
  (iii) $c = 3.2$ and $d = 1.4$.

c) $S = 15 - 3p$. Find S when
  (i) $p = 2$ **(ii)** $p = 5$ **(iii)** $p = 4.2$.

5 Estimating and reading scales

Estimating

To estimate lengths, masses and capacities it is useful to know some standard measures.

The height to a man's waist is about 1 m (100 cm) and his height is about 1·7 or 1·8 m.

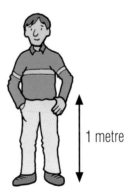

1 metre

The mass of a bag of sugar is 1 kg.

SUGAR

1 kg

A hand is about 10 cm wide.

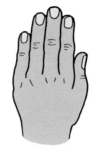

A spread out hand is about 20 cm wide.

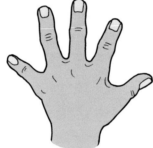

A cup holds about 150 ml.

A small tin of beans weighs about 200 g.

Large bottles of lemonade are mostly 2 litres.

Chapter 5   *Estimating and reading scales*

EXAMPLE 1

Estimate the following.

a) the height of a door   **c)** the length of a car

b) the mass of a cup of flour   **d)** the capacity of a glass of Coke.

a) 2 m = 200 cm

> **Any answer from about 190 to 220 cm is acceptable. Think of a man going through a door.**

b) 150 g

> **Any answer from about 100 g to 300 g is acceptable. It is obviously a lot less than a kilogram.**

c) 4 m

> **Any answer from about 3 to 5 m is acceptable. It will vary with the size of car but is about the length of two men.**

d) 300 ml or 30 cl

> **Any answer from 200 to 500 ml is acceptable. Sizes of glasses vary but they obviously contain a lot less than a litre.**

Sometimes a picture is given and you are asked to estimate a height or length by comparing it with a known height.

EXAMPLE 2

Estimate the height of the lamp.

7·5 m

> **Any answer from 6·5 to 8·5 m would be acceptable. The lamp post is about four times the height of the man and you know the height of the man is about 1·8 m.**

ACTIVITY 1

Match each length with the best and nearest estimate.

Length of pencil	200 km
Length of garden	1 m
Length of M25	10 m
Height of spade	15 cm
Length of car	200 m
Width of house	30 m
Length of High Street	4 m

Exam tip

When estimating do not try to be too accurate. What is wanted is a rough estimate and anything about right is acceptable. Decide if it is bigger or smaller than a measure you know and work from there.

EXERCISE 5.1A

For questions 1 to 8, estimate in metric units.

1 The height of your classroom.
2 The height of a double-decker bus.
3 The length of your foot.
4 The mass of two apples.
5 The mass of a man of average height.
6 The capacity of a tea cup.
7 The capacity of a bucket.
8 The distance you can walk in an hour.

Exercise 5.1A cont'd

9 Estimate
   a) the height of the fence   **b)** the length of the fence.

10 The car is 3·8 m long. Estimate the length of the lorry.

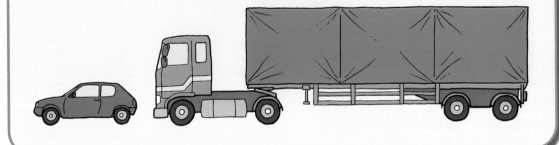

Chapter 5 *Estimating and reading scales*

EXERCISE 5.1B

For questions 1 to 8, estimate in metric units.

1 The length of your classroom.

2 The height of a bungalow.

3 The length of a football pitch.

4 The length of your arm.

5 The mass of a shopping bag full of potatoes.

6 The mass of sugar in a sugar basin.

7 The capacity of a pint pot.

8 The amount of water in a bath.

9 Estimate the height of the tree in metres.

10 Estimate the length of the table.

Reading scales

To read a scale, decide what each small division is and work it out from there.

EXAMPLE 3

What are the readings at A and B on the scale below?

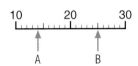

A 14, B 25

Here there are 10 divisions between 10 and 20 so each small division is 1. If the marked lines had been 1, 2 and 3 instead of 10, 20 and 30, each small division would have been 0·1 and A would be 1·4 and B 2·5.

EXAMPLE 4

a) What is the reading at C on the scale below?

b) Mark 63 with a letter D.

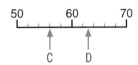

a) C 56

Here there are 5 divisions ('gaps') between 50 and 60 so each is 10 ÷ 5 = 2. If the labels were 1 and 2, each division would be 0·2 and C would be 5·6.

b) D is marked at 63.

The divisions are at 62 and 64 so D is midway between them.

EXAMPLE 5

a) Read the point on the scale marked E.

b) Mark 6·9 with letter F.　5　6　7

a) E 5·6

Here there are two divisions between 5 and 6 so each is 0·5 and to read or mark points you need to judge where they are between the given lines.

E is between 5·5 and 6, and obviously much nearer to 5·5 than 6. The best answer is 5·6 but 5·7 could also be accepted here.

b) F marked at 6·9.

Exam tip

Most errors in reading scales are made because the smallest division is assumed to be 0·1 or 1 or 10, etc. Make sure what the smallest division is before starting reading or marking on a scale.

EXERCISE 5.2A

1 Read the points marked A and B on this scale.

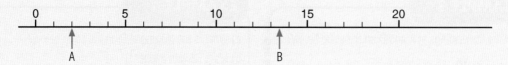

2 Read the points marked C and D on this scale.

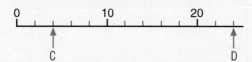

3 Read the points marked E and F on this scale.

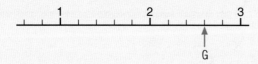

4 **a)** Read the point marked G on this scale.

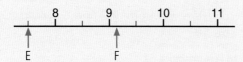

b) Copy the scale and mark point H at 0·7.

5 **a)** Read the point marked I on this scale.

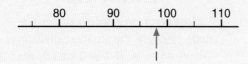

b) Copy the scale and mark point J at 106.

Exercise 5.2A cont'd

6 **a)** Read the point marked K on this scale.

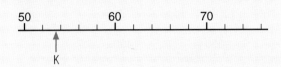

b) Copy this scale and mark the points L 65 and M 73.

7 **a)** Read the point marked N on this scale.

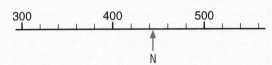

b) Copy this scale and mark the points O 340 and P 515.

8 Read the scale on this thermometer.

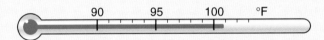

9 Read the amounts on these meters.

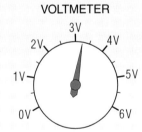
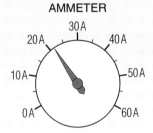

10 How much do these weigh?

a)

b)

c)

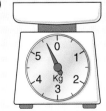

EXERCISE 5.2B

1 Read the points marked A and B on this scale.

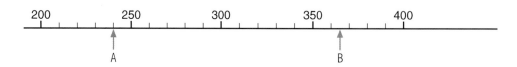

2 Read the points marked C and D on this scale.

3 Read the points marked E and F on this scale.

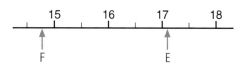

4 a) Read the point marked G on this scale.

b) Copy the scale and mark point H at 63.

Exercise 5.2B cont'd

5 a) Read the point marked I on this scale.

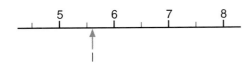

b) Copy the scale and mark point J at 4·8.

6 a) Read the point marked K on this scale.

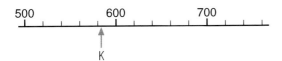

b) Copy this scale and mark the points L 670 and M 715.

7 a) Read the point marked N on this scale.

b) Copy this scale and mark the points O 0·44 and P 0·53.

8 Read the scale on this thermometer.

Chapter 5 *Estimating and reading scales*

Exercise 5.2B cont'd

9 What are the readings on these speedometers?

a)

b)

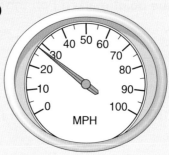

c)

10 Copy these dials and mark the pointers showing the given amounts.

a) 8 Volts   **b)** 1·8 A

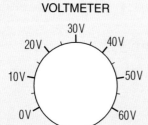

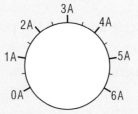

Key ideas

- When estimating, do so by comparing with a known measure.
- To read scales correctly, always check what the smallest division represents.

6 *Fractions*

You should already know

- fraction notation
- how to multiply and divide by whole numbers with and without a calculator.

Converting fractions to decimals

ACTIVITY 1

You probably already know that $\frac{1}{2}$ is equivalent to 0·5.

Check on your calculator that $1 \div 2 = 0.5$.

Other fractions can be changed into decimals in the same way.

Work out on your calculator $3 \div 4$. You should get 0·75.

This means that $\frac{3}{4} = 0.75$.

Work out the decimals for these fractions.

$\frac{1}{4} =$ $\frac{1}{2} =$ $\frac{2}{3} =$

$\frac{1}{8} =$ $\frac{2}{5} =$ $\frac{3}{5} =$ $\frac{4}{5} =$

You are expected to know these so it is best to learn them.

You should also know that the first column after the decimal point means 'tenths'

and so $0.1 = \frac{1}{10}$, $0.2 = \frac{2}{10}$, $0.3 = \frac{3}{10}$ and so on.

Calculating a fraction of a quantity

Fractions with 1 as the top number

EXAMPLE 1

Find $\frac{1}{5}$ of 30

Finding $\frac{1}{5}$ of a quantity means the same as dividing the quantity into 5 equal parts.

So $\frac{1}{5}$ of 30 is the same as $30 \div 5 = 6$.

So $\frac{1}{5}$ of 30 = 6.

EXAMPLE 2

Find $\frac{1}{8}$ of 72

$72 \div 8 = 9$

So $\frac{1}{8}$ of 72 = 9

Fractions with other top numbers

A fraction like $\frac{4}{5}$ simply means 4 lots of $\frac{1}{5}$ or $4 \times \frac{1}{5}$.

So to find $\frac{4}{5}$ of a quantity, simply find $\frac{1}{5}$ of it and multiply by 4.

EXAMPLE 3

Find $\frac{4}{5}$ of 40

$\frac{1}{5}$ of 40 = 40 ÷ 5 = 8

So $\frac{4}{5}$ of 40 = 8 × 4 = 32

EXAMPLE 4

Find $\frac{3}{7}$ of 28

$\frac{1}{7}$ of 28 = 28 ÷ 7 = 4

So $\frac{3}{7}$ of of 28 = 3 × 4 = 12

Exam tip

To find a fraction of something ($\frac{a}{b}$), divide by b and multiply by a.

EXERCISE 6.1A

1 Find $\frac{1}{3}$ of 18.

2 Find $\frac{1}{8}$ of 32.

3 Find $\frac{1}{7}$ of 84.

4 Find $\frac{1}{5}$ of £35.

5 Find $\frac{5}{9}$ of 63.

6 Find $\frac{3}{8}$ of 56.

7 Find $\frac{7}{11}$ of 220.

8 Find $\frac{2}{3}$ of 960.

9 Find $\frac{5}{6}$ of 48 m.

10 Find $\frac{4}{7}$ of £63.

11 Fred is buying a TV and video for £600 The shop needs a deposit of $\frac{1}{3}$. How much is the deposit?

12 In a class of 30, $\frac{4}{5}$ are right-handed. How many is this?

13 In a pantomine audience $\frac{7}{8}$ are children The total audience is 400. How many are children?

14 A shop advertises in a sale '$\frac{1}{4}$ off everything'. A CD player normally costs £68. How much would it cost in the sale?

EXERCISE 6.1B

1 Find $\frac{1}{4}$ of 76.

2 Find $\frac{1}{2}$ of 156.

3 Find $\frac{1}{9}$ of 567.

4 Find $\frac{1}{7}$ of £91.

5 Find $\frac{7}{8}$ of 480.

6 Find $\frac{5}{6}$ of 534.

7 Find $\frac{8}{11}$ of 616.

8 Find $\frac{4}{9}$ of 648.

9 Find $\frac{5}{6}$ of 426 m.

10 Find $\frac{4}{7}$ of £850.50.

11 In a school of 858 pupils $\frac{5}{11}$ are boys. How many boys are there?

12 In a test 45 marks were awarded. Samina got $\frac{2}{3}$ of the marks. How many marks did Samina get?

13 In an election the winning party got $\frac{5}{9}$ of the votes. There was a total of 28 134 votes. How many votes did the winning party get?

14 A survey found that $\frac{5}{12}$ of the people asked had watched Westenders. The total number surveyed was 1068. How many of them had watched Westenders?

Key ideas

● To find a fraction such as $\frac{1}{4}$ of something, divide by 4.

● To find a fraction such as $\frac{4}{5}$ of something, divide by 5 and multiply by 4.

● Simple decimal equivalents to thirds, quarters and fifths should be learnt.

7 Probability

You should already know

- probabilities are always numbers between 0 and 1
- impossibility is represented by a probability of 0
- certainty is represented by a probability of 1
- 'evens' is a probability of $\frac{1}{2}$ or 0·5.

ACTIVITY 1

This game is a version of 'Play Your Cards Right'.

Play in teams of two or three. Each team plays for points.

Five cards are stuck to the board (Blu Tack) or placed on the desk face down. The one at the left-hand end is turned over. You can play or stick. 'Stick' means that you get the points won so far. Each time you have to guess whether the next unseen card is higher or lower than the previous one. If you are right you move on to the next one until you fail (0 points) or stick. The team with the most points wins.

Points 1	2	4	8	16

ACTIVITY 2

This is a version of Animal Olympics.

You play this game in two teams.

You have 30 cards numbered 1 to 30 and each team has five places where they can place the cards.

The cards are shuffled and placed face down. Each team picks one card in turn and puts it in an appropriate place. Cards cannot be moved. The cards must be placed in order, lowest one on the left. If there is no place to put a card, then the team cannot use the card and must discard it. For example, if your team already has and then draws the 20,

	5		18	23

it cannot be placed in order and you have to discard it. The team with all five places filled, i.e. five cards in order, wins.

Calculating probability

What is the probability of getting a tail when you toss a fair coin?

There is an equal likelihood of getting a head and a tail. So there are two equally likely outcomes. The probability of getting a tail is $\frac{1}{2}$ or 0·5.

If you roll a fair dice there are six equally likely outcomes. So the probability of getting a six is $\frac{1}{6}$.

EXAMPLE 1

Find the probability of getting a number less than 3 when you roll a fair dice.

As before, there are six equally likely outcomes. You are interested in getting a number less than 3 so you are interested in getting a 1 or a 2. These are two of the equally likely outcomes. The probability equals $\frac{2}{6}$ or $\frac{1}{3}$.

If you have a set of equally likely outcomes then the probability of an event is given by

$$\text{Probability of event} = \frac{\text{number of outcomes which give the event}}{\text{total number of outcomes}}$$

Exam tip

It is very important to make sure that the outcomes are equally likely. For instance, in the case of a dice, it must be a fair dice.

It is important that probabilities are written as fractions or decimals. For instance $\frac{1}{2}$ and 0·5 are equally acceptable, but '1 in 2' and 'evens' are not.

Since most probabilities are worked out from fractions, it is probably easier to leave them as fractions.

EXERCISE 7.1A

1 Find the probability of getting a 5 when you throw a fair dice.

2 Find the probability of getting a number greater than 1 when you throw a fair dice.

3 The spinner in the picture is fair.
What is the probability of getting

a) a five   **b)** an odd number?

4 There are six blue balls and four red balls in a bag. You take one out without looking. What is the probability of getting a red ball?

5 There are seven blue balls, three red balls and ten yellow balls in a bag. You take one out without looking. What is the probability of getting

a) a red ball   **b)** a yellow ball?

6 Your next dentist's appointment is equally likely to be on any weekday (not Saturday or Sunday). What is the probability of it being on

a) a Monday   **b)** a day beginning with T?

7 A letter is chosen at random from the word REPRESENT. What is the probability that it is

a) an E   **b)** an R?

8 There are seven blue socks and five black socks in a laundry bag. If a sock is chosen at random what is the probability that it is blue?

9 A student is equally likely to be born on any day of the week. What is the probability that a student chosen at random was born on a Friday?

10 A student is equally likely to be born in any month.

a) If this statement is true, what is the probability that a student chosen at random was born in May

b) Why is this statement unlikely to be true?

EXERCISE 7.1B

1   Find the probability of getting an even number when you throw a fair dice.

2   Find the probability of getting a number less than 5 when you throw a fair dice.

3   The spinner in the picture is fair.

What is the probability of getting

   a) a 5   **b)** a number greater than 3?

4   There are 15 green balls and 5 yellow balls in a bag.
You take one out without looking.
What is the probability of getting

   a) a green ball   **b)** a blue ball?

5   There are six blue balls, five green balls and three pink balls in a bag.
You take one out without looking. What is the probability of getting
   a) a blue ball   **b)** a pink ball?

6   There are 20 numbers on a dartboard 1, 2, 3, 4, … 20. If you are equally likely
to hit any number, what is the probability of hitting

   a) 20   **b)** a number less than 10   **c)** a multiple of 6?

7   A letter is chosen at random from the word PERCENTAGE. What is the
probability that it is
   a) an E   **b)** a vowel?

8   Two hundred tickets are sold for a raffle. If you bought one ticket, what is the
probability that you win first prize?

9   Michael says that the probability that City's next match is on a Saturday
is $\frac{1}{7}$. Why is he almost certainly wrong?

10 A card is chosen at random from a normal set of 52 playing cards. What is the
probability that it is

   a) a heart   **b)** a 4?

Key ideas

● **Probabilities can be found from looking at equally likely outcomes.**

● **Probability of event = number of outcomes which give the event**
                        total number of outcomes

8 Conversion graphs

You should already know

- how to plot points on a grid using coordinates
- how to read scales.

EXAMPLE 1

According to the newspaper £1 is worth 1·6 dollars.

This means that £100 is equal to 160 dollars.

This is plotted on the graph below and joined to (0,0)

This is the conversion graph for pounds (£) to dollars ($).

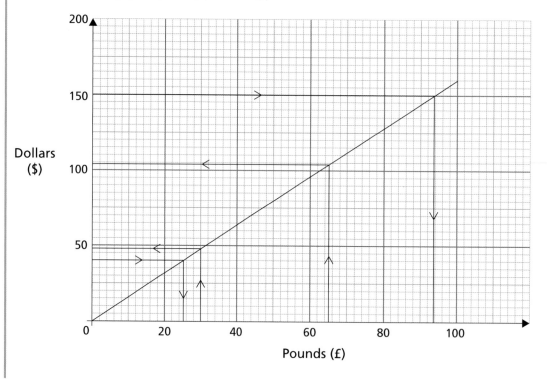

Example 1 cont'd

Use the graph to find   **a)** the number of dollars equal to   **(i)** £30   **(ii)** £65
                         b) the number of pounds equal to   **(i)** $40   **(ii)** $150.

a)   (i) £30 = $48

> The line is drawn up from 30 and across. It meets the $ axis just below 50. Each square of the grid is $5 and the line is less than half a square below $50 at about $48. You cannot read it very accurately and any answer between $45 and $50 would be accepted in an exam.

(ii) £65 = $104

> £65 is $2\frac{1}{2}$ squares across from $60 and the answer is just less than 1 square above $100, at about $104. Here $101 to $105 would be acceptable.

b)   (i) $40 = £25

> $40 is 2 squares below $50 and the answer is between 2 and 3 squares past £20. Any answer between £24 and £26 would be accepted.

(ii) $150 = £93.80

> The answer here is between £92 and £94, but nearer £94. Any answer between £93 and £94 would be accepted.

Exam tip

When reading from a graph, always make sure what each small division stands for. Draw any lines as accurately as you can, but do not try to read the answer to too many figures, as using a graph is not very accurate.

EXERCISE 8.1A

When drawing graphs in this exercise use 2 cm/2 mm graph paper.

1 Write down the coordinates of the points labelled A, B, C and D on the graph.

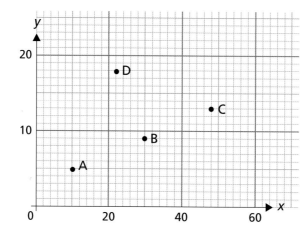

2 Write down the coordinates of the points labelled P, Q, R and S on the graph.

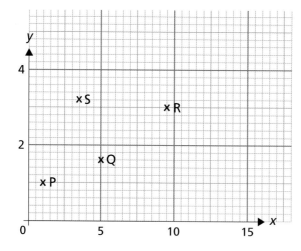

Exercise 8.1A cont'd

3 Copy this graph onto graph paper.

Plot and label the points.
A (20, 100),
B (50, 90),
C (64, 140),
and D (35, 105).

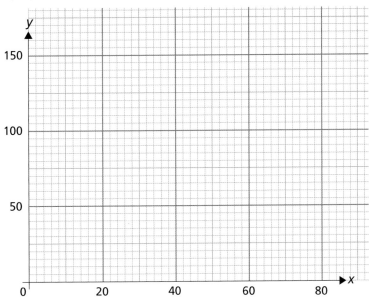

4 On a piece of graph paper mark axes.

Horizontally 0 to 50, using 2 cm for 10 units.

Vertically 0 to 20 using 2 cm for 5 units.

Plot and label these points A (5, 10), B (30, 8), C (33, 17) and D (47, 14·5).

5 The table below shows the distance in kilometres a car travels in given times (in hours).

Time (h)	0	2	4	6	8
Distance (km)	0	110	220	330	440

a) Plot the points on a graph.

Put time on the horizontal axis. Use a scale of 1 cm to 1 hour.
Put distance on the vertical axis. Use a scale of 1 cm to 50 km.
Join the points with a straight line.

b) Find the distance travelled after
(i) 3 h   **(ii)** 5·5 h.

c) Find the time taken to travel
(i) 385 km   **(ii)** 80 km.

001466 · HODDER · GCSF MATHS FOR OCR 3-4 · SEGN 3

Exercise 8.1A cont'd

6 This conversion graph is for pounds (£) to euros (€) for amounts up to £20.

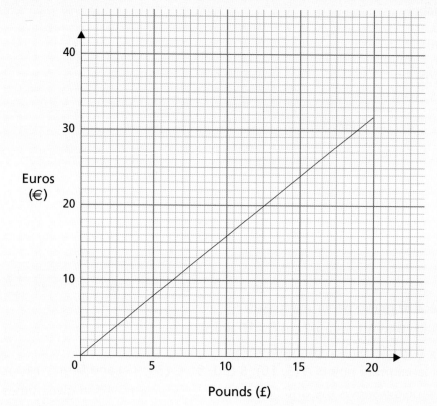

Use the graph to find

a) the number of euros equal to
   (i) £5
   (ii) £12

b) the number of pounds equal to
   (i) € 15
   (ii) € 29.

Exercise 8.1A cont'd

7 This conversion graph is for pounds (£) to French francs (F) for amounts up to £100.

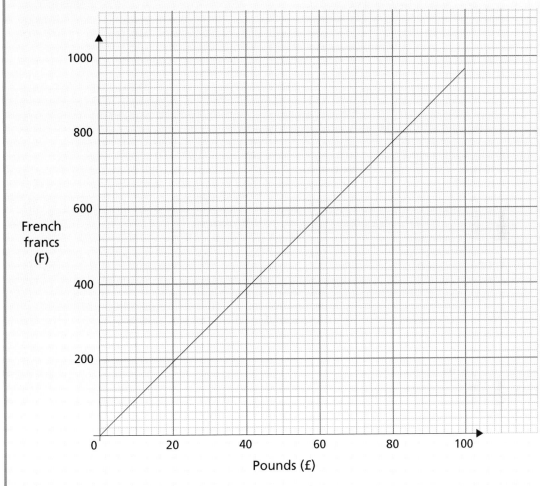

Use the graph to find

a) the number of French francs equal to
   (i) £50
   (ii) £80

b) the number of pounds equal to
   (i) F 400
   (ii) F 750.

Exercise 8.1A cont'd

8 This conversion graph is for the number of kilometres (km) equal to miles up to 100 km.

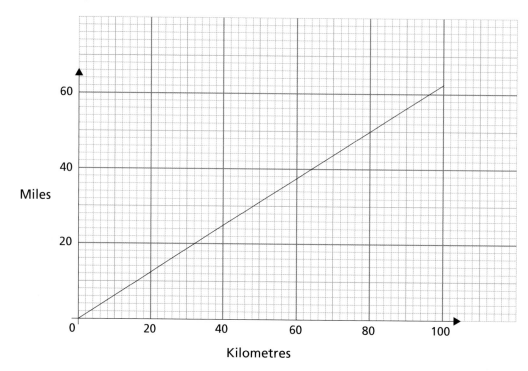

Use the graph to find

a) the number of miles equal to
   (i) 40 km
   (ii) 65 km

b) the number of kilometres equal to
   (i) 10 miles
   (ii) 56 miles.

Exercise 8.1A cont'd

9 This conversion graph is for pints to litres up to 50 pints.

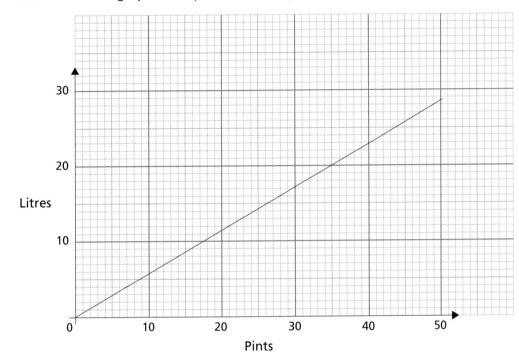

Use the graph to find
a) the number of litres equal to
    (i) 10 pints
    (ii) 45 pints
b) the number of pints equal to
    (i) 10 litres
    (ii) 18 litres.

Exercise 8.1A cont'd

10 This graph shows the temperature of a substance cooling from 80 °C.

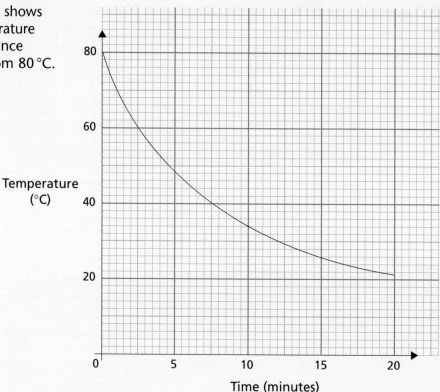

a) What is the temperature after
   (i) 5 minutes   **(ii)** 12·5 minutes?

b) What time has passed when the temperature is
   (i) 34 °C   **(ii)** 25 °C?

11 A newspaper states that one French franc (F) is equal to 6·3 Belgian francs (BF).

a) On a piece of graph paper, mark axes horizontally for French francs up to F50, using 2 cm to F10, and vertically for Belgian francs up to BF350 using 2 cm to BF100.

b) Plot the point (50, 315) and join to (0, 0).

c) Find the number of Belgian francs equal to
   (i) F40   **(ii)** F16.

d) Find the number of French francs equal to
   (i) BF150   **(ii)** BF220.

EXERCISE 8.1B

When drawing graphs in this exercise use 2 cm/2 mm graph paper.

1 Write down the coordinates of the points labelled A, B, C and D on the graph.

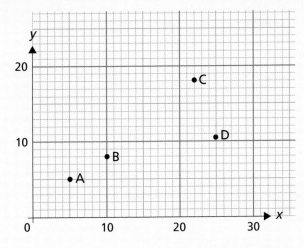

2 Write down the coordinates of the points labelled P, Q, R and S on the graph.

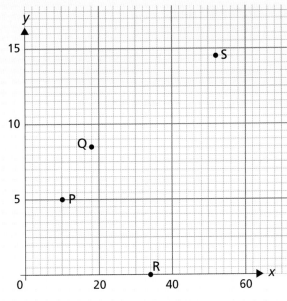

Exercise 8.1B cont'd

3 **a)** Write down the coordinates of the points labelled A, B, C on the graph.

b) On a copy of the graph, plot and label the points D (1, 2·5) E (4, 1·8) and F (5·5, 2·8).

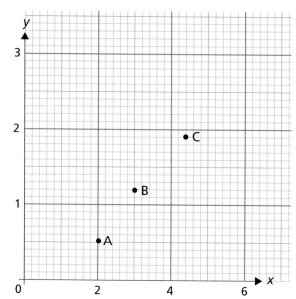

4 On a piece of graph paper mark the axes.

Horizontally 0 to 30, using 2 cm for 5 units.

Vertically 0 to 40 using 2 cm for 10 units.

Plot and label these points A (5, 10), B (8, 18), C (23, 35) and D (27·5, 24).

5 The table shows the number of litres of fuel left after a car has travelled a certain number of kilometres.

Distance travelled (km)	0	50	100	150	200	250
Fuel left (l)	35	30	25	20	15	10

a) Plot the points on a graph.

Put distance on the horizontal axis. Use a scale of 2 cm to 50 km.

Put Fuel left on the vertical axis. Use a scale of 1 cm to 5 l.

Join the points with a straight line.

b) Find the fuel left after

(i) 80 km   **(ii)** 170 km.

c) Find the the distance travelled when the amount of fuel left is

(i) 32 l   **(ii)** 12 l.

Exercise 8.1B cont'd

6   This conversion graph is for pounds (£) to German Marks (DEM) for amounts up to £100.

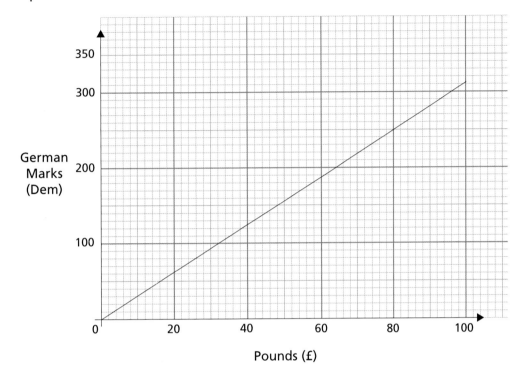

Use the graph to find

a) the number of German Marks equal to
(i) £20
(ii) £85

b) the number of pounds equal to
(i) Dem 100
(ii) Dem 250.

Exercise 8.1B cont'd

7 This conversion graph is for French francs (F) to Israeli shekels (iS) for amounts up to F100.

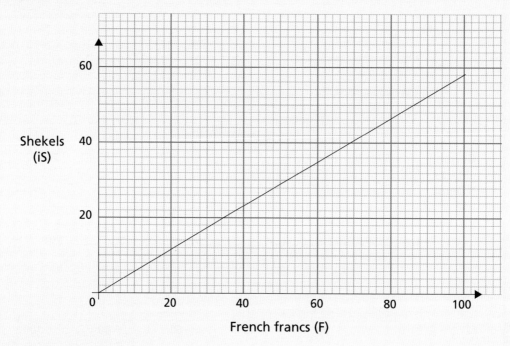

Use the graph to find

a) the number of shekels equal to
    (i) F40
    (ii) F90

b) the number of francs equal to
    (i) iS40
    (ii) iS18.

Exercise 8.1B cont'd

8 This conversion graph is for pounds to kilograms, for up to 100 pounds.

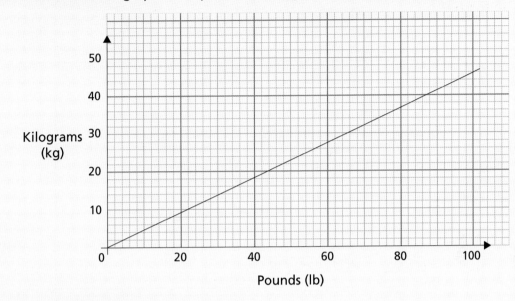

Use the graph to find

a) the number of kilograms equal to
(i) 20 lb
(ii) 75 lb

b) the number of pounds equal to
(i) 40 kg
(ii) 25 kg.

Exercise 8.1B cont'd

9 This conversion graph is for temperatures in °C to °F, from 0 to 100 °C.

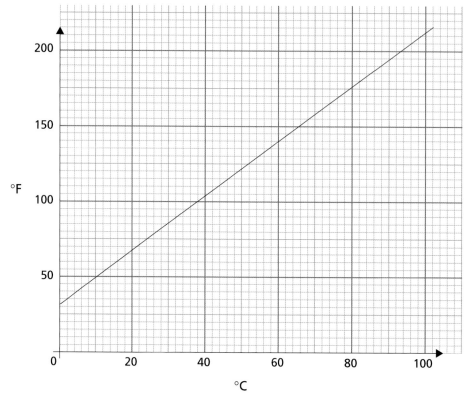

Use the graph to find
a) the temperature in °F equal to
 (i) 0 °C
 (ii) 85 °C
b) the temperature in °C equal to
 (i) 100 °F
 (ii) 170 °F.

Exercise 8.1B cont'd

10 This graph is for petrol consumption in cars and gives the consumption in miles per gallon (mpg) equal to litres per 100 kilometres (l/100 km) for consumption between 10 and 60 miles per gallon.

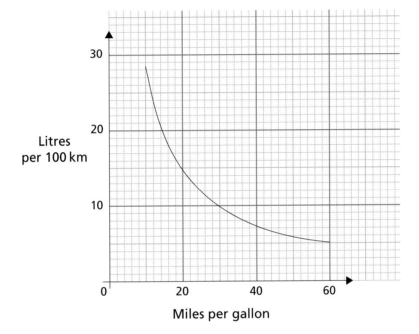

Use the graph to find

a) the consumption in litres per 100 km equivalent to
   (i) 20 mpg
   (ii) 45 mpg

b) the consumption in miles per gallon equal to
   (i) 8 litres per 100 km
   (ii) 20 litres per 100 km.

Exercise 8.1B cont'd

11 One pound is equal to 0·64 Maltese lire.

   a) On a piece of graph paper, mark axes horizontally for pounds up to £100 (use a scale of 2 cm to £20), and vertically for Maltese lire up to 80 lire (use a scale of 2 cm to 20 lire).

   b) Plot the point (100, 64) and join it to (0, 0) with a straight line.

   c) Find the number of Maltese lire equal to

      (i) £45

      (ii) £85.

   d) Find the number of pounds equal to

      (i) 20 Maltese lire

      (ii) 45 Maltese lire.

Key ideas

- When plotting and reading off graphs, always check the scale.
- When converting from the quantity on the horizontal axis, draw a line up to meet the graph and then across to meet the vertical axis.
- When converting from the quantity on the vertical axis, draw a line across to meet the graph and then down to the horizontal axis.

B1 Revision exercise

1 Estimate using metric units
   a) the length of a swimming pool
   b) the length of a chair leg
   c) the mass of a jar of jam
   d) the capacity of a soup bowl
   e) the capacity of the kitchen sink
   f) the mass of an egg
   g) the length of the bristles on a toothbrush.

2 a) Estimate the height of the kite above the ground.
   b) Estimate the length of the kite string.

3 Read the points marked on these scales.
   a)

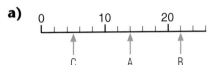

   b)

   c)

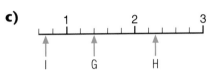

4 a) Copy this scale and mark the points A 3·5 and B 1·8.

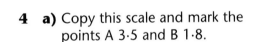

   b) Copy this scale and mark the points C 140 and D 187.

   c) Copy this scale and mark the points E 45, F 71 and G 89.

5 Read the points marked on these scales.

a)

b)

c)

6 Find   **a)** $\frac{1}{4}$ of 284   **b)** $\frac{1}{7}$ of 56

c) $\frac{4}{5}$ of 60   **d)** $\frac{3}{8}$ of 72

e) $\frac{5}{11}$ of 330   **f)** $\frac{5}{6}$ of 894.

7 A shop advertises '$\frac{1}{3}$ off everything' in a sale. A television normally costs £399. What is the reduction in the sale?

8 $\frac{7}{8}$ of the people watching a football match were males. If 8400 people watched the match, how many were males?

9 A test was marked out of 60. Bilal got $\frac{7}{12}$ of the marks. How many did Bilal get?

10 The spinner in the picture is fair. What is the probability of getting
a) a 1   **b)** a 3?

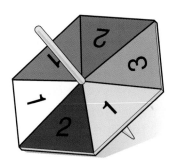

11 There are five red balls, six blue balls and four green balls in a bag.
If a ball is chosen without looking, what is the probability that it is
a) red   **b)** blue?

12 A letter is chosen at random from the word PROBABILITY. What is the probability that it is
a) a B   **b)** an L?

13 There are 25 daffodil bulbs, 40 crocus bulbs and 10 hyacinth bulbs in a bag. If a bulb is chosen at random, what is the probability that it is
a) a crocus   **b)** a hyacinth?

14 This conversion graph is for dollars ($) to pounds (£) up to $80.

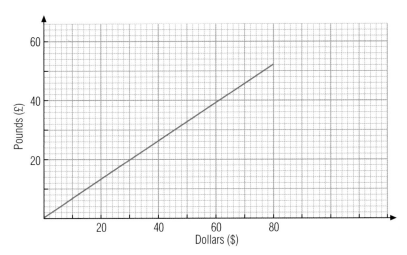

Use the graph to find

a) the number of pounds equal to   **(i)** $40   **(ii)** $25

b) the number of dollars equal to   **(i)** £40   **(ii)** £32.

15 On a piece if gaph papermark the axes horizontally 0 to 1000 grams using 2 cm to 200 grams. Vertically 0 to 40 ounces using 2 cm to 10 ounces. Join the points (0, 0) to (1000, 35). This graph can be used to convert between grams and ounces.

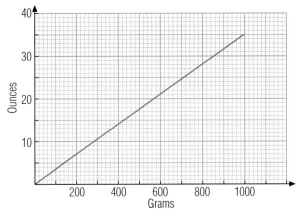

Use the graph to find

a) the number of ounces equal to   **(i)** 200 g   **(ii)** 900 g

b) the number of grams equal to   **(i)** 4 ounces   **(ii)** 20 ounces.

9 *Area*

You should already know

- how to find the area of shapes by counting squares
- that the units of area are cm², m², km².

Area of a rectangle

ACTIVITY 1

Find the area of these rectangles. Each small square has sides 1 cm long.

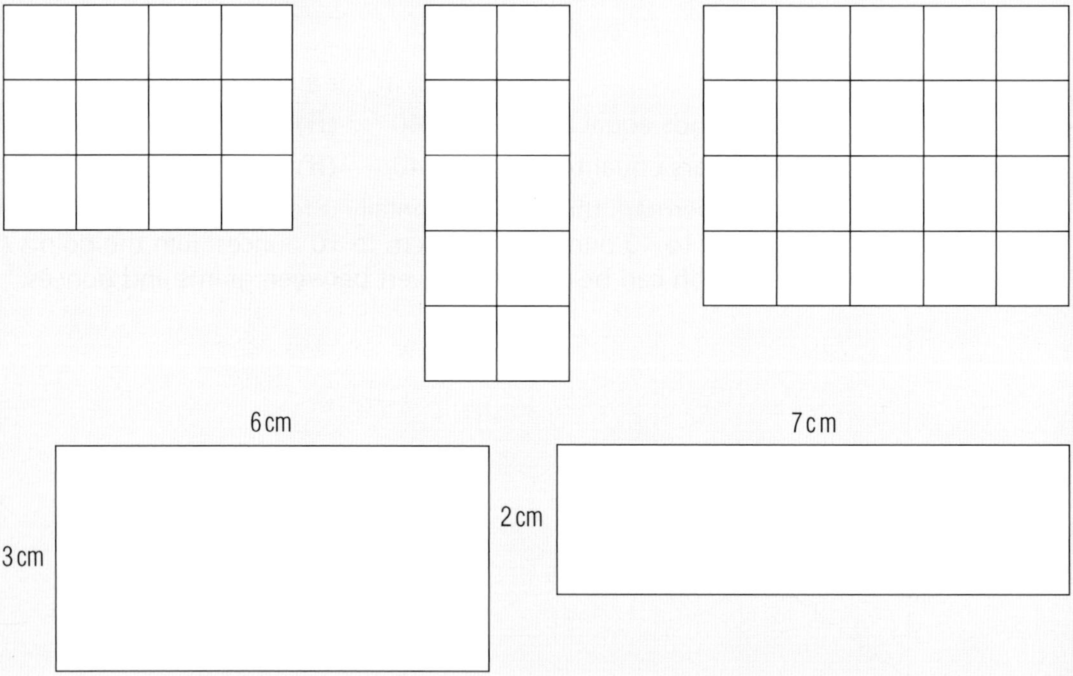

6 cm

3 cm

7 cm

2 cm

Can you find a quick way of finding the area?

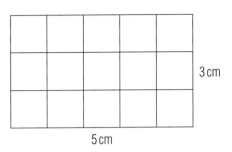

3 cm

5 cm

In this rectangle there are three rows. Each row has five squares. The total number of squares is
$$3 \times 5 = 15.$$
So the area is 15 cm^2.

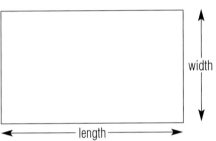

width

length

For rectangles of any size
Area of rectangle = length × width

Exam tip

Whenever you are giving an answer for an area, make sure you put the units in. If the lengths are in cm, the area will be in cm^2. If the lengths are in m, the area will be in m^2.

EXAMPLE 1

Find the area of the rectangle below.

8 m

4 m

Area = 8 × 4
  = 32 m^2

Notice that the lengths are given in metres (m), so the area will be in metres squared or square metres (m^2).

EXAMPLE 2

Find the area of a square of side 7·2 cm.

7·2 cm

7·2 cm

Area = 7·2 × 7·2
  = 51·84 cm^2

Draw a sketch first and label the sides. A sketch does not have to be accurate – it is just to help you picture the shape.

73

EXERCISE 9.1A

1 Find the area of the following rectangles. Take care to give the correct units in your answer.

a)

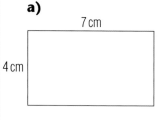

7 cm

4 cm

b)

6 km

6 km

c)

25 mm

4 mm

2 Find the area of the following rectangles.

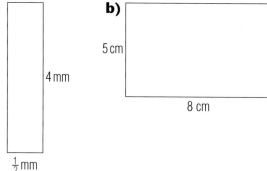

a)

4 mm

½ mm

b)

5 cm

8 cm

c)

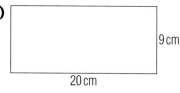

9 cm

20 cm

d)

30 m

30 m

3 My living room measures 8 m long by 4 m wide.

a) Calculate the area of the floor.

Carpet costs £5 per square metre.

b) How much will it cost to buy carpet for my living room?

4 The perimeter of a square is 28 cm. Calculate its area.

5 A bathroom wall measures 2 m by 2·5 m.

a) Work out the area of the wall **in cm²**.

A tile measures 10 cm by 10 cm.

b) Work out the area of one tile in cm².

c) How many tiles will be needed to cover the wall?

EXERCISE 9.1B

1 Find the area of these rectangles. Take care to give the correct units of your answer.

a)
1·6 cm
5 cm

b)
0·5 m
6·4 m

c)
8·4 cm
5·9 cm

2 Find the area of these rectangles.

a)
1·5 cm
1·5 cm

b)
7·3 cm
4·2 cm

c)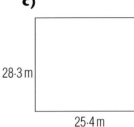
28·3 m
25·4 m

d)
48 km
123 km

3 An airport is built on a rectangular piece of land 1·8 km long and 1·3 km wide. Calculate

   a) the area of the land

   b) the length of fencing needed to go round the perimeter of the airport.

4 A rectangle has an area of 240 cm². One of its sides is 16 cm long. Calculate the length of the other side of the rectangle.

5 A rectanglular lawn measures 24 m by 18·5 m.

   a) Work out the area of the lawn.

   Lawn weedkiller is spread on the lawn. 50 g of weedkiller is needed for every square metre.

   b) How many kilograms of weedkiller are needed to treat the whole lawn?

   c) Weedkiller is sold in 2·5 kg boxes. How many boxes must I buy?

ACTIVITY 2 – EXTENSION

Find the area of these shapes by splitting them up into rectangles.

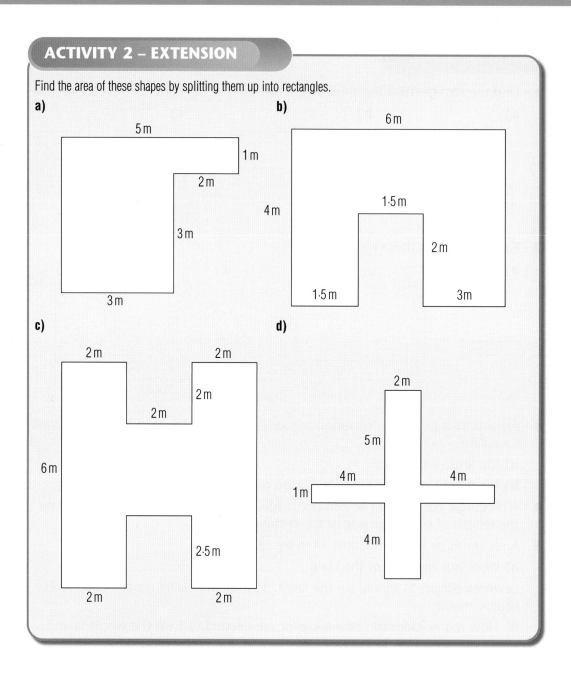

a)

b)

c)

d)

Area of a right-angled triangle

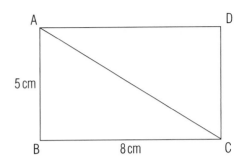

The area of the rectangle ABCD is $8 \times 5 = 40 \text{ cm}^2$.

The area of the triangle ABC is half the area of the rectangle ABCD and so is equal to 20 cm^2.

So the area of the right-angled triangle
$= \frac{1}{2} \times 8 \times 5 = 20 \text{ cm}^2$.

The area of a right-angled triangle
$= \frac{1}{2} \times \textbf{base} \times \textbf{height.}$

EXERCISE 9.2A

1 Find the area of these right-angled triangles. Remember to state the units.

a)

3 cm
4 cm

b)

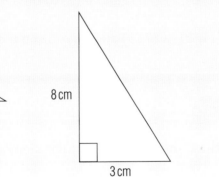
8 cm
3 cm

c)

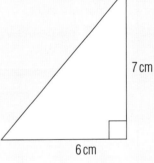
7 cm
6 cm

d)

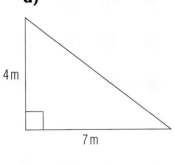
4 m
7 m

e)

8 m
2 m

f)

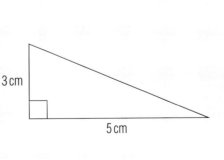
3 cm
5 cm

Exercise 9.2A cont'd

g)

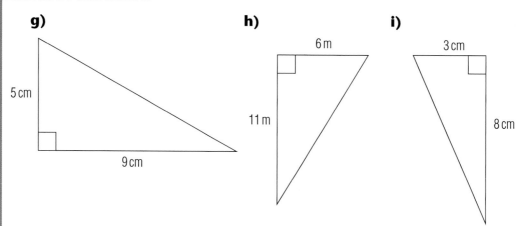

h)

i)

2 Plot the points A (1, 1), B (5, 1) and C (5, 3) on a grid. Calculate the area of triangle ABC.

3 Plot the points P (2, 3), Q (7, 3) and R (2, 6) on a grid. Calculate the area of triangle PQR.

4 Plot the points W (1, 2), X (1, 5) and Y (7, 5) on a grid. Calculate the area of triangle WXY.

EXERCISE 9.2B

1 Find the areas of these right-angled triangles. Remember to state the units.

a)

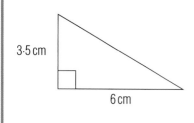

b)

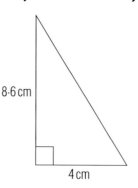

c)

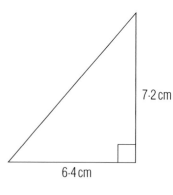

Exercise 9.2B cont'd

d)

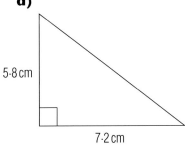

e)

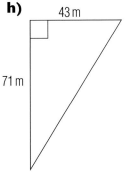

f)

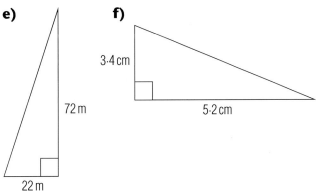

g)

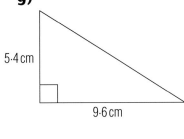

h)

i)

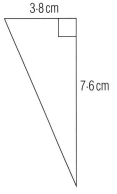

2 Plot the points A (2, 1), B (8, 1) and C (8, 6) on a grid. Calculate the area of triangle ABC.

3 Plot the points P (1, 7), Q (8, 7) and R (8, 2) on a grid. Calculate the area of triangle PQR.

4 Find the area of this shape.

Key ideas

● The area of a rectangle = length × width.

● The area of a right-angled triangle = $\frac{1}{2}$ × base × height.

10 Mean and range

You should already know

- how to add, subtract, multiply and divide numbers
- the meaning of 'mode' and 'median' for a set of numbers.

Averages and spread

Tariq and Farhat go ten-pin bowling. These are their scores.

Tariq	7	8	5	4	7
Farhat	10	10	2	1	6

The **mean** is the total of the scores divided by the number of games.

The mean for Tariq is $31 \div 5 = 6 \cdot 2$

The mean for Farhat is $29 \div 5 = 5 \cdot 8$

The **range** is the difference between the highest score and the lowest score.

The range for Tariq is $8 - 4 = 4$

The range for Farhat is $10 - 1 = 9$

Tariq has a smaller range so his scores are more consistent.

Farhat has a larger range so her scores are more spread out.

ACTIVITY 1

Four darts players take practice throws (of three darts) and record the scores.

A	67	101	32	74	32	54
B	36	31	29	37	35	
C	52	41	83	23	47	
D	35	41	24	140	46	38

Work out the mean and range for each. Who is the best player?
Who is the most consistent and who is the least consistent.

Exam tip

Just because all the values are whole numbers, it does not follow that the mean is a whole number. It could be a decimal.

1 Find the mean and range of marks for each of these tests.

a) 3   5   6   7   9

b) 8   9   4   3   7   3   1   7

c) 7   8   8   8   8   7   7   8   8   8

2 The time taken for a bus journey depends on the time of day.

Here are the times in minutes.

15   7   19   12   9

19   6   11   9   14

What is the mean and the range of the times?

3 12 people have their hand spans measured. The results are shown below.

225 mm   216 mm   188 mm   212 mm   205 mm   198 mm

194 mm   180 mm   194 mm   198 mm   200 mm   194 mm

a) How many of the group had a hand span greater than 200 mm?

b) What is the range of the hand spans?

c) What is the mean hand span?

d) How do these figures compare with people in your Maths group?
Measure hand spans and find out.

4 The PE staff of a school measure the time, in seconds, it takes the football team and hockey team to run 100 m.

Football team

13 14 15 11 14 12 12 13 11 13 14

Hockey team

12 13 14 11 12 14 15 13 15 14 11

a) Calculate the mean and range for both teams.

The PE staff are then timed running over the same distance.

Their times, in seconds, are

12   11   13   15   11

b) Which group do you think is faster?

5 The number of matches in ten different matchboxes were

48 47 47 50 46 50 49 49 47 50

a) find the mean   **b)** find the range.

Exercise 10.1A cont'd

6 Write down five numbers with a mean of 15 and a range of 6.

7 **a)** Nine pupils scored a mean of 7 marks for their last Maths test. What was their total mark?

b) A tenth pupil scored 10. What was the mean mark of all 10?

EXERCISE 10.1B

1 Copy and fill in the table below for each of the sets of data.

Data set A   1, 1, 2, 2, 3, 3, 3, 4, 5, 6, 7

Data set B   1, 1, 2, 2, 3, 3, 3, 4, 5, 6, 7, 1, 1, 2, 2, 3, 3, 3, 4, 5, 6, 7

Data set C   2, 2, 4, 4, 6, 6, 6, 8, 10, 12, 14

	Data set A	Data set B	Data set C
Range			
Mean			

Write down anything that you notice about these results.

2 **a)** Find the mean of

(i) 1, 2, 3, 3, 4, 5   **(iii)** 110, 120, 120, 130, 170

(ii) 10, 20 20, 30, 70   **(iv)** 7, 10, 13, 16, 19

b) What do you notice about your answers to **(ii)** and **(iii)**?

3 In a survey of TV watching, a group of boys and girls wrote down how many hours of TV they watched each week.

Boys	17	22	21	23	16	12	15
	0	5	13	15	13	14	20
Girls	9	13	15	17	10	12	11
	9	8	12	14	15		

a) Find the mean and range for these figures.

b) Do the boys watch more than the girls?

c) Do a survey to see what the figures are for your group.

Exercise 10.1B cont'd

4 The pay of 10 workers in a small company is

£10 000	£10 000	£10 000	£10 000	£13 000
£13 000	£15 000	£21 000	£23 000	£70 000

a) Find the mean for the data.

b) Why do you think the mean gives a misleading impression of the average pay?

c) You have previously learnt two other measures of average, the mode and the median. Would either of these give a better impression of average pay? If so why?

5 The marks scored in a test were

20	16	18	17	16	18	14	13
18	18	15	18	19	9	12	13

a) Find the mean.

b) Find the range.

6 Write down six numbers with a mean of 20 and a range of 9.

7 **a)** 18 houses had a mean of 2·5 letters delivered. What was the total number of letters?

b) Another two houses had 5 and 7 letters delivered. What was the mean number of letters delivered for all 20 houses?

Key ideas

In a set of data

- the mean is the 'usual' average and is found by adding up all the values and dividing by the number of values.
- the range is the difference between the smallest and largest values. It is a measure of how spread out the values are.

11 Percentage

You should already know

- percentage notation
- that $\frac{1}{2} = 50\%$ and $\frac{1}{4} = 25\%$ and how to calculate 50% and 25% of a quantity.

Calculating a percentage of a quantity

Method 1

EXAMPLE 1

Find 20% of £8.

Since 20% means 20 out of 100 or $\frac{20}{100}$ you can find a percentage of a quantity in the same way that you found a fraction of a quantity in Chapter 6.

This means that you need $\frac{20}{100}$ of £8.

£8 ÷ 100 = 8 p

8p × 20 = 160p = £1.60

So 20% of £8 = £1.60.

Method 2

EXAMPLE 1 (AGAIN)

Find 20% of 8.

The same calculation can be done using decimals.

$\frac{20}{100} = \frac{2}{10} = 0{\cdot}2$

$8 \times 0{\cdot}2 = 1{\cdot}6$

So 20% of £8 = £1.60

In this method you simply multiply by the decimal equivalent of the percentage.

In the same way

The decimal equivalent of 30% = 0·3

The decimal equivalent of 15% = 0·15

The decimal equivalent of 5% = 0·05

The methods above can be used for any percentages and method 2 is particularly useful when you have a calculator.

When you have no calculator a third method is useful for simple percentages like 10%, 20%, or 5%.

Method 3

EXAMPLE 1 (AGAIN)

Find 20% of £8.

Since 10% = $\frac{20}{100}$ = $\frac{1}{10}$ it is very easy to find 10%

£8 = 800p so 10% of 800p = 800 ÷ 10 = 80p

20% is then 2 × 80p = 160p = £1.60

EXAMPLE 2

Find 15% of £240.

10% of £240 = 240 ÷ 10 = £24

5% of £240 = half of £24 = £12

So 15% of £240 = £24 + £12 = £36

EXAMPLE 3

Find 30% of £6.80.

£6.80 = 680p

10% of 680p = 680 ÷ 10 = 68p

$$30\% \text{ of } 680 = \begin{array}{r} 68 \\ \times\ 3 \\ \hline 204 \\ {\scriptstyle 2} \end{array}$$

So 30% of £6.80 = 204p = £2.04

Exam tip

If you are not using a calculator and the percentages are fairly easy ones like 5%, 10%, 15%, 20% and 30%, the last method is probably the easiest.

EXERCISE 11.1A

1 10% of £200.

2 Find 10% of £6.

3 Find 10% of £7.20.

4 Find 20% of £30.

5 Find 30% of £60.

6 Find 20% of £5.

7 Find 20% of £300.

8 Find 30% of £18.

9 Find 30% of £8.60.

10 Find 5% of £40.

11 Find 5% of £300.

12 Find 5% of £6.80.

13 Find 15% of £400.

14 Find 15% of £12.

15 Find 15% of £7.20.

16 Find 15% of £12.50.

17 10% of the 640 pupils in a school are left-handed. How many pupils is this?

18 A salesman gets 15% commission on sales of £600. How much is his commission?

19 Which is more, 15% of £60 or 20% of £50? Show your working.

Exercise 11.1A cont'd

20 A shop increases its DVD prices by 5%. What is the increase on a DVD which had originally cost £20?

21 20% of the pupils in a school arrive by bus. There are 800 pupils in the school. How many arrive by bus?

EXERCISE 11.2A

1 Find 10% of £300.

2 Find 10% of £4.

3 Find 10% of £8.40.

4 Find 20% of £70.

5 Find 30% of £40.

6 Find 20% of £3.

7 Find 20% of £400.

8 Find 30% of £16.

9 Find 30% of £6.40.

10 Find 5% of £60.

11 Find 5% of £700.

12 Find 5% of £4.60.

13 Find 15% of £500.

14 Find 15% of £14.

15 Find 15% of £5.80.

16 Find 15% of £8.50.

17 A school gave 10% of the money raised from a 'non-uniform' day to a charity. The total raised was £120. How much did the charity receive?

18 A shop requires 15% deposit on a case which costs £40. How much is the deposit?

19 Which is more, 15% of £20 or 20% of £15? Show your working.

20 A charity spends 5% of their income on administration. If they receive £8 000, how much is spent on administration?

21 500 people took part in a transport survey. 15% of them wanted spending on transport increased. How many is this?

Key ideas

- 20% means 20 out of 100 = $\frac{20}{100}$.
- To find 20% of a quantity, multiply by $\frac{20}{100}$ or by the decimal equivalent 0·2.
- A quick way of finding 20% of a quantity is to first find 10% and then multiply by 2.
- Similar methods to the above are used for 5%, 15%, 30% and so on.

Drawing three-dimensional shapes

You should already know

- how to recognise simple solid shapes, e.g. cube, cuboid, pyramid.

This shape is a cuboid (rectangular block).

Drawing and constructing
As well as a ruler, a protractor or an angle measure and a pair of compasses, a set-square is useful.

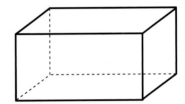

On the real block all the faces are rectangles.
When you are drawing this block on paper it is impossible to make all the faces rectangles.
First draw the top as a parallelogram.

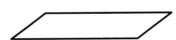

Drawing parallel lines
Parallel lines are always the same distance apart.

Now draw vertical lines from each corner. Make sure all the lines are the same length.
Now draw lines joining the bottoms of these vertical lines.

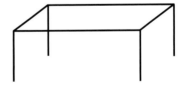

This is now quite a good picture of the block.

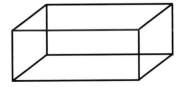

To make it even better, change the edges that are hidden from view into dotted lines.

This is called an oblique projection of the block, but you do not have to remember this name.

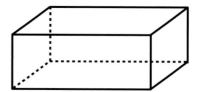

EXAMPLE 1

Draw a square-based pyramid.

1)

First draw the square base as a parallelogram.

2)

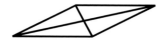

Now find the middle of the parallelogram by drawing the diagonals.

3)

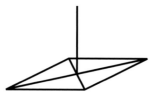

Now draw a line vertically upwards from the middle of the base

4)

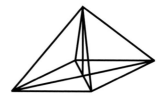

Now join the top of this line to the four corners of the base.

In Mathematics you may often be told to leave construction lines in diagrams to help you with calculations.

If you want to make the diagrams more realistic, you can rub out the construction lines and make hidden edges dotted.

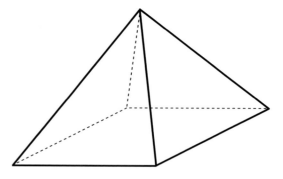

EXAMPLE 2

Make a drawing of a cylinder.

The top of the cylinder is a circle, but you need to draw it as an oval.

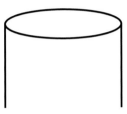

Now draw vertical lines for the sides. Make sure they are the same length.

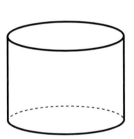

Now draw an oval for the base. Make the hidden back of the base dotted.

Exam tip

In all these drawings the horizontal faces need to be drawn 'flattened'. In the rectangular block and the pyramid the bases have to be parallelograms. In the cylinder the circular base and top have to be drawn as an oval.

89

Chapter 12 *Drawing three-dimensional shapes*

EXERCISE 12.1A

1 Draw these shapes. Add in the hidden edges as dotted lines.

a)

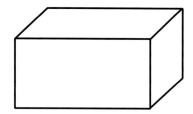

b)

c)

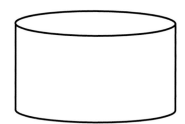

d)

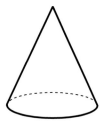

e) Pyramid with rectangle base

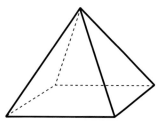

f) Tetrahedron

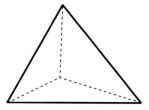

EXERCISE 12.1B

1 Draw these shapes. Add in the hidden edges as dotted lines.

a)

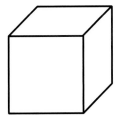

b)

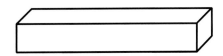

c) Square based pyramid

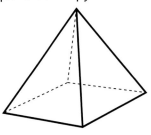

d)

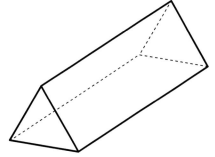

e)

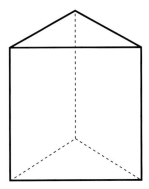

f)

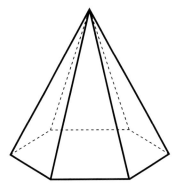

Chapter 12 *Drawing three-dimensional shapes*

Isometric drawings

For these drawings, you will need a ruler, a pencil and triangle spotty paper.

Isometric drawing is a way of representing 3D shapes. Triangle spotty paper is ideal for this.

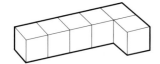

Exam tip

Make sure that the spotty paper is the right way round. Draw in pencil, then any mistake can be put right.

EXAMPLE 1

Look at this shape.

This is an isometric drawing of the same shape.

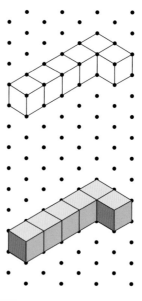

You can make the drawing look more realistic and easier to understand by using different shadings for the sides facing in the three different directions.

EXERCISE 12.2A

Draw these shapes on triangle spotty paper.
Make sure your paper is the correct way round.

1

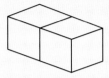

4

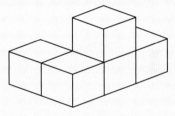

2

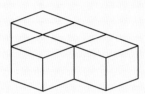

5

3

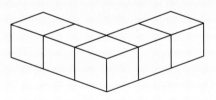

6 A cuboid with dimensions 5 by 2 by 4.

Chapter 12 *Drawing three-dimensional shapes*

EXERCISE 12.2B

1 This shape is made from 4 cubes. Draw all the possible arrangements of 4 cubes with faces touching. There are 7 more.

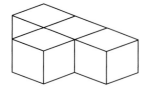

2 Draw these shapes on triangle spotty paper.

a)

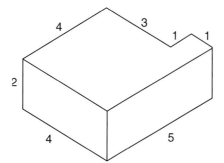

b)

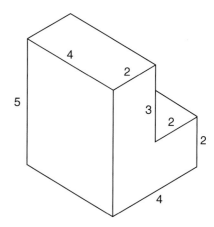

Key ideas

● When drawing oblique projections, horizontal faces have to be 'flattened'. Vertical edges remain vertical.

● When drawing isometric diagrams use triangle spotty paper. Make sure you have it the right way round.

Revision exercise

1 Find the area of these rectangles.

a)

7 cm
3 cm

b)
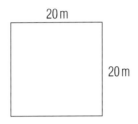
20 m
20 m

c)
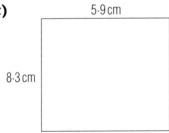
5·9 cm
8·3 cm

2 Find the area of these right-angled triangles.

a)
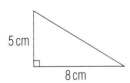
5 cm
8 cm

b)
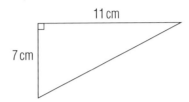
11 cm
7 cm

c)
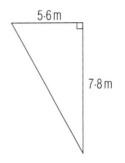
5·6 m
7·8 m

3 Calculate the shaded area between these two rectangles.

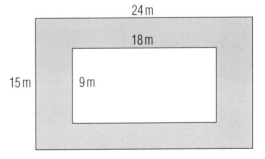
24 m
18 m
15 m
9 m

4 Measure the sides of a piece of A4 paper. Find its area.

5 The time in minutes that two groups of children took to solve a puzzle were

Group A 8 9 5 6 7
 3 10 2 6 9

Group B 6 6 8 9 5
 6 7 6 7 5

Find the mean and range for each of the groups. What do you notice?

6 The results in Maths tests of two groups of pupils are

Group A

17	31	32	35	28
36	58	60	48	50
53	45	37	56	10
13	49	55	27	35
29	52	57	40	47

Group B

44	10	35	46	36
43	33	35	44	47
39	42	60	33	34
49	47	38	48	35
45	40	37	41	39

Compare these results using mean and range.

7 **a)** Find the mean and range for this set of data.

 2 5 7 6 9 8 3 5

b) Find the mean and range for this set of data.

 102 105 107 106
 109 108 103 105

8 Write down six numbers with a mean of 10 and a range of 8.

Do not use a calculator for questions 9–12.

9 Calculate

a) 10% of £630

b) 15% of £84

c) 30% of £7

d) 5% of £240

e) 20% of £6.70.

10 In a sale a shop reduces all prices by 20%. Find the reduction on a fleece normally costing £35.

11 Jasvindar gets a wage increase of 5%. She previously earned £120 per week. What will the increase be?

12 30% of a school's pupils come to school by bus. If the school has 650 pupils, how many come by bus?

13 Draw these shapes.

a)

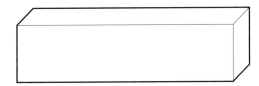

b)

c)

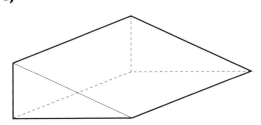

14 Draw these shapes on triangle spotty paper. (Make sure your paper is the right way round.)

a)

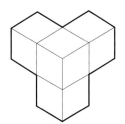

b)

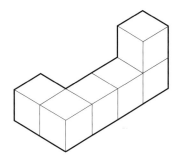

c)

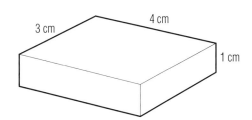

97

Collecting and illustrating data

You should already know

- how to make tally charts
- how to draw simple bar charts.

You may have seen headlines like these in newspapers or on the television:

B*Witched is the most popular group

or

Teenagers vote Diet Coke as the best soft drink

You may not agree with either headline but how is such information found out?

One way is to ask people questions – that is, to carry out a survey using a **questionnaire** and collect the answers on a **data collection** sheet. The answers are then analysed to give the results.

Collecting data, tallying and using frequency tables

EXAMPLE 1

Julie wants to find out how many people are in cars that pass the school gates each day between 8.30 a.m. and 9.00 a.m.

(i) She writes down the number of people in the first 40 cars that pass on the first Monday

1	2	4	1	1	3	1	2	2	3
4	2	1	1	1	2	2	3	2	1
1	1	2	2	1	3	4	1	1	1
2	1	3	3	1	1	4	2	1	2

Example 1 cont'd

(ii) Julie now makes a tally chart to show her results and calculates the totals.

Number of people	Tally	Total
1	⳽⳽⳽ ⳽⳽⳽ ⳽⳽⳽ ///	18
2	⳽⳽⳽ ⳽⳽⳽ //	12
3	⳽⳽⳽ /	6
4	////	4

These totals are the frequencies

> **Because the totals are included, this is known as a frequency table.**
>
> **Remember to group the tally marks into fives, which are shown like this:**
> ⳽⳽⳽ **for easier counting.**

In Example 1 it would have been simpler and perhaps more reliable to have collected the data directly onto the tally chart. (Why, do you think?)

Simple tally charts are very easy to use when you need to collect numbers of 'things'.

EXAMPLE 2

For several weeks John keeps a record of how many minutes his train is late each morning.

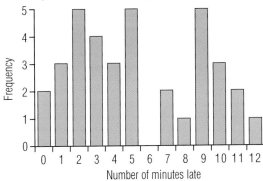

a) How many days was his train 4 minutes late?   **a)** 3

b) How many days was his train 10 minutes late?   **b)** 3

c) How many days was his train on time?   **c)** 2

d) For how many days did John keep a record?   **d)** $2+3+5+4+3+5+2+1+5+3+2+1=36$

Chapter 13 *Collecting and illustrating data*

Vertical-line graphs

The graph in Example 2 is a simple bar chart. When you are dealing with whole-number information it is sometimes more useful to draw a 'vertical-line graph'.

Look again at the table in Example 1.

Number of people	Total
1	18
2	12
3	6
4	4

On a vertical-line graph, vertical lines are drawn instead of bars. Vertical-line graphs are sometimes called 'stick graphs'. They should only be drawn for 'whole-number' information.

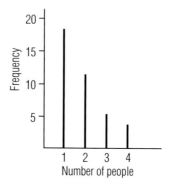

EXERCISE 13.1A

1 The following numbers of letters delivered one morning to 80 houses.

0	2	5	3	1	2	0	3	4	7
2	1	0	0	1	4	6	3	2	1
5	3	2	1	1	2	0	3	2	7
1	2	0	3	5	2	0	1	1	2
2	0	1	2	0	2	1	0	0	3
8	1	6	2	0	1	1	2	3	2
0	1	2	6	2	4	1	0	3	2
2	1	4	0	1	2	3	1	4	0

a) Make a tally chart and record the totals.

b) Draw a bar chart to show this information.

Exercise 13.1A cont'd

2 These are the scores of 50 golfers in a competition.

72	76	75	78	75	76	80	79	78	76
71	73	74	77	78	76	75	70	72	73
74	79	78	77	73	72	71	76	70	73
74	75	75	73	72	79	78	76	72	74
71	73	76	74	78	72	73	73	75	76

a) Make a tally chart and record the totals.

b) Draw a bar chart to show this information.

3 This table shows the number of pets owned by the children in 3C.

Number of pets	0	1	2	3	4	5	6
Number of children	5	10	8	4	2	0	1

Show this information

a) on a vertical-line graph

b) on a bar chart.

4 The numbers of peas in 60 pods are

8	7	6	8	7	4	9	8	7	7
6	8	9	8	5	6	8	7	8	6
5	6	8	9	8	7	5	8	6	7
9	6	10	8	7	6	5	3	8	9
6	8	7	7	8	8	6	9	7	8
7	6	8	9	4	7	8	6	8	7

a) Make a tally chart and record the totals.

b) Draw a bar chart to show this information.

5 The table below shows the number of people in 100 cars that pass the school gate.

Number of people	1	2	3	4	5	6
Number of cars	48	25	16	8	2	1

Show this information

a) on a bar chart

b) on a vertical-line graph.

Chapter 13 *Collecting and illustrating data*

EXERCISE 13.1B

This exercise should be done in pairs or groups.

1   **a)** Make a tally chart to find the shoe sizes of the students in your class, form or year. Before you start,

    (i)   think about the sizes that might be worn

    (ii) do you need to think about half-sizes?

    (iii) do you need to separate males and females?

   b) Now do the survey and show your results in a bar chart.

2   Choose a topic – either from the list below or one of your own.

    (i)   Design a questionnaire.

    (ii) Design a data collection sheet.

    (iii) Carry out a survey.

    (iv) Show your findings in a bar chart or vertical-line graph.

Possible topics:

- the most popular music group among your class/group or year
- the number of people living in a house
- are more babies born at certain times of the year?
- the prices of second-hand cars
- the most popular soft drink.

3   Jane is reading a holiday brochure. She counts the numbers of letters in each word in the following passage

Excellent onboard facilities include live entertainment, cinema, disco, first class cuisine, ships, cafes, bars, nightclub and a wide range of comfortable cabins. Prices are based on two people sharing a two berth inside cabin with shower and wc. Other cabin prices are available.

Exercise 13.1B cont'd

Jane shows her findings in this bar chart.

a) How many 4-letter words were there?

b) How many words were there in the passage?

c) How many words in the passage had more than 6 lettters?

d) Find a passage in a book or newspaper and compare numbers of letters in the same number of words as in Jane's passage above.

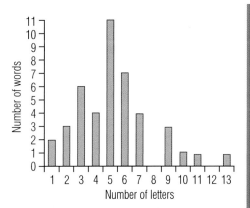

4   Choose two newspapers. It may be best to choose one broadsheet (e.g. *The Times, Telegraph, Guardian*) and one tabloid newspaper (e.g. *Sun, Mirror, Mail*).

Choose an article from the same section of the paper, for example sport or fashion.

a) Count the number of words in the sentences and make a tally chart. It would look like this.

Newspaper 1

Number of words	Tally	Total
3	/	1
4	///	3
5	//// //	7
6	etc.	etc.
7		
etc.		

b) Draw a bar chart for each of the newspapers.

c) Write down anything you notice about your results.

Key ideas

● Surveys are carried out to find information and test statements.

● Tally charts are used to find frequencies of the results of a survey.

● Tables of frequencies can be represented on bar charts and vertical-line graphs.

14 Order of operations

You should already know

- how to add, subtract, multiply and add ordinary numbers
- that, for example, 3^2 means $3 \times 3 = 9$.

To use a calculator and to get the right answer when there is more than one operation to do, you need to know in what order to press the keys.

Work out in your head

$$6 \times 4 + 3 = 27$$

$$3 + 6 \times 4 =$$

The answer should still be 27. Try it on your calculator.

In Mathematics you don't just work from left to right. Instead, you should multiply before you add. This is algebraic logic. Scientific calculators use this logic. However, many basic calculators work from left to right.

It may help you to remember the acronym BOMDAS.

Brackets	are done first
Of **M**ultiplication **D**ivision	are done next
Addition **S**ubtraction	are done last

The '**O**f' in the table above refers to calculations like '$\frac{3}{4}$ of 36'. You will not need it in this chapter.

The **BOMDAS** rule works like this: to write or work out $3 + 6 \times 4$, where you mean 'Add 3 and 6 first and then multiply the result by 4', you can use brackets: $(3 + 6) \times 4 = 9 \times 4 = 36$

If your calculator has brackets, you can use those. Otherwise, try this key sequence to do this calculation:

$\boxed{3}$ $\boxed{+}$ $\boxed{6}$ $\boxed{=}$ $\boxed{\times}$ $\boxed{4}$ $\boxed{=}$

EXAMPLE 1

Work out
a) $4 + 5 \times 2 - 1$
b) $5 \times (6 - 2)$

a) $4 + 10 - 1 = 13$

> **Remember to do the multiplcation first.**

b) $5 \times 4 = 20$

> **This time because it is in a bracket, do the subtraction first.**

EXAMPLE 2

Work out $4 \times 2 \cdot 6 + 3 \cdot 5^2$

$4 \times 2 \cdot 6 + 3 \cdot 5^2 = 10 \cdot 4 + 12 \cdot 25 = 22 \cdot 65$

> **Remember that $3 \cdot 5^2$ means $3 \cdot 5 \times 3 \cdot 5$. You can work this out using either the × button or the 'square' button if your calculator has one.**

EXAMPLE 3

Work out $\dfrac{9 \cdot 5 + 4 \cdot 7}{5 \cdot 67 - 4 \cdot 96}$

> **For fractions like this work out the top part (numerator) and bottom part (denominator) first, before dividing. The fraction line acts like a bracket.**

$$\frac{9 \cdot 5 + 4 \cdot 7}{5 \cdot 67 - 4 \cdot 96} = \frac{14 \cdot 2}{0 \cdot 71} = 20$$

EXERCISE 14.1A

If you have a scientific calculator you can check your answers at the end using your calculator.

1 **a)** $3 + 5 \times 2$ **b)** $6 + 5 \times 7$ **c)** $5 \times 4 - 8$
   d) $4 + 6 \times 2$ **e)** $7 + 2 \times 3$ **f)** $5 \times 8 - 4$

2 **a)** $(7 - 4) \times 3$ **b)** $(8 + 2) \times 5$ **c)** $9 - (1 + 2)$
   d) $(7 - 3) \times 5$ **e)** $(6 + 4) \times 5$ **f)** $12 - (2 + 3)$

3 **a)** $\dfrac{4 \times 10}{8}$ **b)** $\dfrac{4 + 12}{8}$ **c)** $\dfrac{12 - 3}{9}$ **d)** $\dfrac{3 \times 10}{6}$ **e)** $\dfrac{6 + 12}{3}$ **f)** $\dfrac{15 - 3}{2}$

4 **a)** $2 + \dfrac{10}{5}$ **b)** $12 - \dfrac{6}{2}$ **c)** $\dfrac{20}{5} - 3$ **d)** $4 + \dfrac{8}{2}$ **e)** $10 - \dfrac{6}{2}$ **f)** $\dfrac{12}{2} - 3$

5 **a)** $14 - 6 \times 2$ **b)** $4 \times 2 + 10$ **c)** $6 + \dfrac{12}{3}$

   d) $18 - 7 \times 2$ **e)** $4 \times 3 + 10$ **f)** $9 + \dfrac{12}{3}$

Extension question

6 Write out these sums, using brackets if necessary, to get the answers stated.
   a) $3 + 6 \times 5 - 1$ to get   **(i)** 44   **(ii)** 32   **(iii)** 27
   b) $12 - 8 \div 4 + 4$ to get   **(i)** 11   **(ii)** 5   **(iii)** 14.

EXERCISE 14.1B

1 Calculate
   a) $2 \cdot 5^2 + 3 \cdot 4^2$ **b)** $4 \cdot 9^2 - 3 \cdot 1^2$ **c)** $12 \cdot 2^2 - 12 \cdot 1^2$
   d) $16^2 + 30^2$ **e)** $5 \cdot 2^2 - 2 \cdot 6^2$ **f)** $8 \cdot 3^2 - 8 \cdot 2^2$

2 Find
   a) $3 \cdot 1 \times 9 \cdot 2 - 14 \cdot 6$ **b)** $3 \cdot 7 + 4 \cdot 1 \times 7 \cdot 8$ **c)** $7 \cdot 5 \times (6 \cdot 2 + 5 \cdot 8)$
   d) $4 \cdot 6 \times 9 \cdot 3 - 24 \cdot 1$ **e)** $2 \cdot 8 + 4 \cdot 7 \times 6 \cdot 9$ **f)** $8 \cdot 1 \times (4 \cdot 2 + 12 \cdot 3)$

3 Calculate
   a) $\dfrac{6 \cdot 9 - 4 \cdot 7}{0 \cdot 11}$ **b)** $\dfrac{7 \cdot 5}{0 \cdot 3 + 1 \cdot 2}$ **c)** $\dfrac{4 \cdot 6 \times 2 \cdot 5}{11 \cdot 5}$

   d) $\dfrac{6 \cdot 72 - 4 \cdot 8}{0 \cdot 12}$ **e)** $\dfrac{6 \cdot 4}{0 \cdot 4 + 1 \cdot 2}$ **f)** $\dfrac{4 \cdot 9 \times 2 \cdot 6}{63 \cdot 7}$

Exercise 14.1B cont'd

4 Work out
   a) $4 \cdot 2 + 9 \cdot 7 \times 14$ **b)** $15 \times (9 \cdot 2 - 5 \cdot 1)$ **c)** $72 - 15 \times 4 \cdot 3$
   d) $5 \cdot 6 + 7 \cdot 8 \times 12$ **e)** $15 \times (8 \cdot 7 - 6 \cdot 5)$ **f)** $84 - 12 \times 4 \cdot 5$

5 Calculate
   a) $16 \cdot 8 + \dfrac{8 \cdot 4}{2 \cdot 1}$ **b)** $\dfrac{41 \cdot 43 - 15 \cdot 6}{2 - 0 \cdot 95}$ **c)** $\dfrac{2 \cdot 4 + 15 \cdot 6}{9 \cdot 2 - 1 \cdot 7}$

   d) $19 \cdot 2 + \dfrac{9 \cdot 6}{2 \cdot 4}$ **e)** $\dfrac{60 \cdot 14 - 8 \cdot 2}{3 - 1 \cdot 04}$ **f)** $\dfrac{5 \cdot 2 + 11 \cdot 7}{5 \cdot 1 - 3 \cdot 8}$

Extension question

6 Write out these sums, using brackets if necessary, to get the answers stated.
   a) $6 + 4^2 - 16 \div 2$ to get   **(i)** 6   **(ii)** 3   **(iii)** 92
   b) $18 + 12 \div 6 - 3$ to get   **(i)** 2   **(ii)** 17   **(iii)** 22   **(iv)** 10.

Key ideas

- Make sure that you are familiar with your calculator and know how to use it.
- When calculations are written down, the meaning depends on the calculations being done in the correct order, namely

  (i) Brackets

  (ii) Multiplication and Division

  (iii) Addition and Subtraction.

15 Scale drawings

You should already know

- how to measure lengths using a ruler
- how to multiply and divide lengths by whole numbers.

Scale drawings keep exactly the shape of the original drawing but are 'scaled down' in size so that, for example, they can fit onto the page of a book.

The scale of the drawing is written like this:

1 cm to 2 m

This means that every 1 cm on the scale drawing is representing 2 m in real life.

EXAMPLE 1

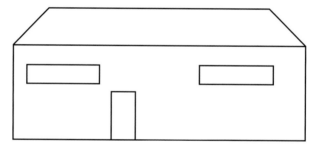

This is a picture of Emma's bungalow. It is drawn to a scale of 1 cm to 2 m.

a) How wide is the real window on the left?

b) How high is the bungalow?

c) Emma is 1·5 m tall. How big would she be on the scale drawing?

a) The window measures 2 cm wide. In real life it will be $2 \times 2 = 4$ m.

b) The bungalow measures 2·5 cm. In real life it will be $2·5 \times 2 = 5$ m.

c) On the scale diagram Emma's height will be $1·5 \div 2 = 0·75$ cm.

EXERCISE 15.1A

1 Here is a scale drawing of the plan of Emma's bungalow.
The sale is 1 cm to 2 m.

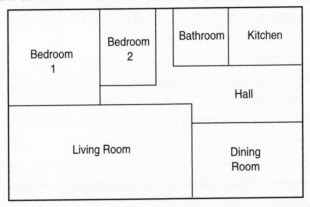

a) Find the length and width of each of the rooms.

b) How long is the hall?

c) The bungalow is on a plot of land measuring 24 m by 15 m. What will be the measurement of the plot of land on this scale drawing?

2 Below is a scale map of the major cities in the north of England.

The scale of the map is 1 cm to 20 km. On the map it is 2·8 cm from Manchester to Sheffield. The real distance is $2.8 \times 20 = 56$ km.

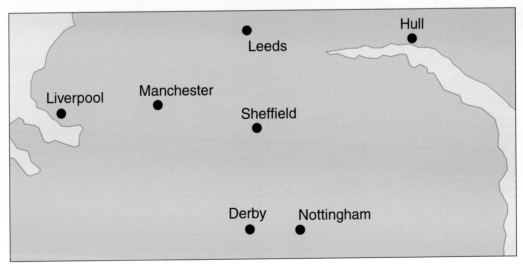

Chapter 15 *Scale drawings*

Exercise 15.1A cont'd

  a) How far is it, in km, from

    (i) Derby to Hull   **(ii)** Liverpool to Sheffield

    (iii) Nottingham to Manchester   **(iv)** Leeds to Derby

    (v) Hull to Liverpool   **(vi)** Sheffield to Nottingham

    (vii) Manchester to Leeds?

  You may need a calculator to help you with some of these.

  b) How far is the round trip from Nottingham to Derby to Manchester to Hull and back to Nottingham?

  c) It is 320 km from Manchester to London. How far would this be on the map?

  d) It is 194 km from Leeds to Birmingham. How far is this on the map?

3 Make an accurate scale drawing of your classroom. Choose a suitable scale to use.

EXERCISE 15.1B

1 Here is the plan of Rebecca's bedroom. The scale of the diagram is 1 cm to 40 cm.

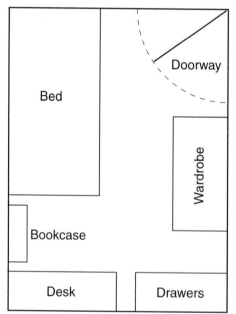

Exercise 15.1B cont'd

    a) Find the real length and width of

        (i) the bedroom   **(ii)** the bed

        (iii) the desk   **(iv)** the wardrobe

        (v) the drawers   **(vi)** the bookcase.

    b) How wide is the doorway?

    c) What does the dashed line represent?

    d) The window in the bedroom measures 80 cm by 140 cm. What would the size of the window be on the scale drawing?

2 Here is a map of southern England and northern Europe. The scale of the map is 1 cm to 50 miles.

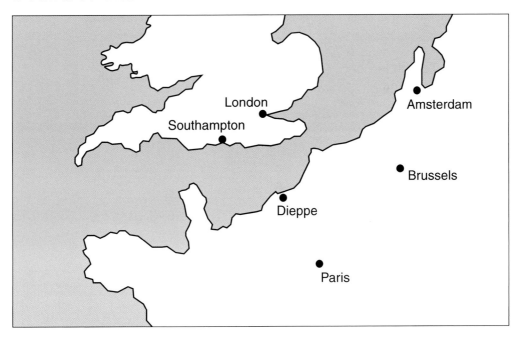

    a) How far is it from:

        (i) Southampton to Brussels   **(ii)** Paris to Brussels

        (iii) London to Amsterdam   **(iv)** London to Paris

        (v) Amsterdam to Southampton   **(vi)** Southampton to Dieppe?

Chapter 15 *Scale drawings*

Exercise 15.1B cont'd

    b) It is 1000 miles from London to Lisbon. What distance would this be on the map?

    c) It is 540 miles from Paris to Berlin. What distance would this be on the map?

3 Draw a plan of your bedroom. Measure the length and width of the room and the things in it. Use a suitable scale and mark these things on your plan. Make it an easy scale and work out the scaled lengths carefully.

Key ideas

- The scale of a drawing is written, for example 1 cm to 2 m. This means that each centimetre on the drawing represents an actual distance of 2 metres.

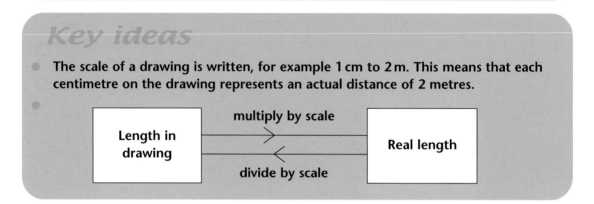

Chapter 15 *Scale drawings*

16 Equations

You should already know

- that letters can be used to represent numbers
- that, for example, $3a$ means $3 \times a$
- that the reverse of + is −
  - − is +
  - × is ÷
  - ÷ is ×

The price of a carton of milk has gone up 5 pence. It now costs 59 pence. How much did it cost before?

Let the original price be c pence.

Then the new price is $c + 5$.

But this is equal to 59, so $c + 5 = 59$.

This is an **equation**.

Solving equations

Look at the above equation $c + 5 = 59$

In this case, the problem can easily be solved without the equation.

If the price of a carton of milk went up by 5 pence to 59 pence, it must have been $(59 - 5)$ pence before, i.e. 54 pence.

The equation has two sides, $c + 5$ and 59. The amounts on either side are equal.

If you subtract 5 from $c + 5$, you are left with c. But then the two sides will no longer have the same value.

To keep them the same, subtract 5 from 59.

Write this as:

$$c + 5 = 59$$
$$[c + 5 - 5 = 59 - 5]$$
$$c = 54$$

With practice you can leave out the line in square brackets.

EXAMPLE 1

Solve the equation $2d = 12$.
$$2d = 12$$
$$[2d \div 2 = 12 \div 2]$$
$$d = 6$$

The d has been multiplied by 2.

To find d, you must halve the $2d$, or divide by 2.

To keep the sides the same, you must also divide the 12 by 2.

EXAMPLE 2

Solve the equation $p - 3 = 7$.
$$p - 3 = 7$$
$$[p - 3 + 3 = 7 + 3]$$
$$p = 10$$

On the left-hand side, 3 has been subtracted from p.

To find p you must add 3.

Exam tip

Always perform the same operation to the whole of each side.

EXERCISE 16.1A

Solve these equations in questions 1 to 11.

1 $3a = 12$

2 $4b = 24$

3 $2c = 16$

4 $d + 1 = 3$

5 $e + 6 = 17$

6 $f + 4 = 13$

7 $g - 3 = 6$

8 $h - 5 = 1$

9 $5 + j = 11$

10 $2k = 17$

11 $x \div 7 = 5$

12 Andy is 16. He is five years older than Barry.

   a) If Barry is b years old, write down an equation with b in it.

   b) Solve the equation in part **a)** to find Barry's age.

13 Five loaves cost 300p.

   a) If l is the cost of one loaf in pence, write down an equation with l in it.

   b) Solve the equation in part **a)** to find the cost of a loaf.

Exercise 16.1A cont'd

14 Usma is slimming. So far she has lost 7 kg. She now weighs 48 kg.

   a) If she weighed w kg before, write down an equation with w in it.

   b) Solve the equation in part **a)** to find what she weighed before.

15 Gary has 34 CDs, which is half as many as Kirsty has.

   a) If k is the number of Kirsty's CDs, write down an equation with k in it.

   b) Solve the equation in part **a)** to find how many CDs Kirsty has.

EXERCISE 16.1B

Solve the equations in questions 1 to 11.

1 $2x = 14$

2 $5y = 35$

3 $4z = 4$

4 $p + 2 = 5$

5 $q + 5 = 16$

6 $r + 3 = 10$

7 $a - 3 = 1$

8 $3b = 18$

9 $3c = 20$

10 $5d = 22$

11 $p \div 6 = 12$

12 Gina is three times as old as Burhan. Gina is 15.

   a) If Burhan is b years old, write down an equation with b in it.

   b) Solve the equation in part **a)** to find Burhan's age.

13 Chloe gets £2 more pocket money than George. Chloe gets £7.

   a) If George gets £g, write down an equation with g in it.

   b) Solve the equation in part **a)** to find how much George gets.

14 Seven packets of crisps cost 168p.

   a) If c is the cost of a packet of crisps in pence, write down an equation with c in it.

   b) Solve the equation in part **a)** to find the cost of a packet of crisps.

15 In a sale a pair of trainers is reduced by £16 to £48.

   a) If the original price of the trainers was £t, write down an equation with t in it.

   b) Solve the equation in part **a)** to find the original cost of the trainers.

Key ideas

● **The two sides of an equation must always be kept equal.**

● **Operations carried out to solve an equation must always be the same for each side.**

D1 Revision exercise

1 On a Biology field trip Hannah recorded the number of a certain plant in 50 different $\frac{1}{2}$ metre squares. The results were

5	1	0	6	3	4	2	1	6	2
2	3	5	0	6	4	5	0	1	1
3	2	0	4	5	4	3	3	0	6
5	4	3	2	4	3	1	2	4	3
7	2	1	3	4	4	3	2	1	5

a) Use tallies to draw up a frequency table for this information.

b) Draw a vertical-line graph to show the information.

c) Which number is the mode?

2 a) Rashid did a survey to find out how often the different vowels appear in a passage from a novel. The results are shown in the tally chart.

Vowel	Tally
A	ⴰⵜⴽ ⵜⴽⵜ ⵜⴽⵜ ⵜⴽⵜ ////
E	ⵜⴽⵜ ⵜⴽⵜ ⵜⴽⵜ ⵜⴽⵜ ⵜⴽⵜ ⵜⴽⵜ ⵜⴽⵜ //
I	ⵜⴽⵜ ⵜⴽⵜ ⵜⴽⵜ //
O	ⵜⴽⵜ ⵜⴽⵜ ⵜⴽⵜ ⵜⴽⵜ ///
U	ⵜⴽⵜ //

(i) Draw up a frequency table for this information.

(ii) Draw a bar chart to show the frequencies.

(iii) Place the vowels in order of their frequencies, highest first.

b) Repeat part a) making a tally chart for a passage in a book of your own. Is the order of the vowels the same?

3 On a certain maker's matchboxes, it says' average contents 48 matches'. A Weights and Measures inspector bought 40 of these boxes to test them. She counted the matches in each box. The results are shown here.

50	47	46	48	48	47	49	50	47	46
48	46	45	48	48	49	50	51	47	48
46	47	50	51	48	48	48	47	50	49
48	47	48	47	50	45	46	47	50	48

a) Use tallies to draw up a frequency table for this information.

b) Draw a vertical-line graph to show the information.

c) Which number is the mode?

d) What is the mean number of matches?

e) Comment on your results.

4 Copy these calculations and put a ring round the first operation done in each calcuation.

a) $3 \cdot 5 + 4 \cdot 2 \times 5 \cdot 1$

b) $\dfrac{4 \cdot 6}{0 \cdot 5} - 2 \cdot 7$

c) $7 + (3 \cdot 2 - 4 \cdot 9)$

5 Find the answers to the complete calculations in question 4.

6 Calculate

   a) $4 \cdot 6 \times (3 \cdot 9 + 104 \cdot 1)$

   b) $\dfrac{2 \cdot 6 + 5 \cdot 2}{0 \cdot 13}$

   c) $\dfrac{4 \cdot 9}{7 - 2 \cdot 1}$

   d) $19 \cdot 6 + \dfrac{11 \cdot 9}{1 \cdot 7}$

   e) $\dfrac{87 \cdot 2 + 72 \cdot 6}{12 \cdot 9 - 3 \cdot 5}$

   f) $\dfrac{93 \cdot 2 - 17 \cdot 6}{5 \cdot 7 - 2 \cdot 9}$

7 Calculate

   a) $(4 \cdot 3 + 5 \cdot 2)^2$

   b) $4 \cdot 3^2 + 5 \cdot 2^2$

   c) $9 \cdot 7^2 - 6 \cdot 3^2$

8 Here is a scale drawing of a house and its garage.

The scale used is 1 cm to 2 m

a) Work out the length and width of

   (i) the house

   (ii) the garage

   (iii) the whole plot of land

b) How far is the house from the garage?

c) How far is the front of the garage from the road?

d) The car is 3·2 m long. How long will it be on the scale drawing?

e) The garden at the back of the house is 29 m long. How long will it be on the scale drawing?

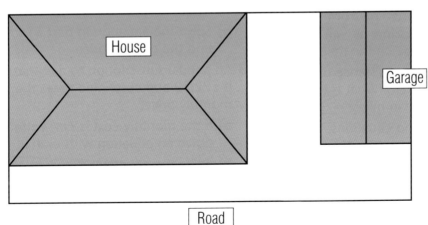

House

Garage

Road

9 The table below shows the distances between various towns and cities.

Cambridge					
337	Edinburgh				
143	288	Leeds			
60	405	196	London		
153	218	43	199	Manchester	
119	249	34	167	36	Sheffield

For example, the distance from Edinburgh to Manchester is 218 miles.

A map is drawn to a scale of 1 cm to 10 miles.

a) How far on the map will it be from
   (i) Cambridge to London
   (ii) Edinburgh to Manchester
   (iii) Leeds to Sheffield?

b) John is travelling from Manchester to Leeds and then on from Leeds to Cambridge. How far will the total journey be on the map?

c) Leslie measures a distance on the map to be 5·8 cm. What is the actual distance in miles?

10 Solve the following equations.

   a) $x + 3 = 12$ b) $a - 7 = 3$
   c) $5p = 45$ d) $b + 6 = 20$
   e) $a \div 6 = 4$ f) $9x = 63$
   g) $b - 9 = 23$ h) $\frac{c}{7} = 6$

11 John is 11 and is 6 years older than Kasim.

   a) If Kasim is k years old, write down an equation with k in it.

   b) Solve the equation in part a) to find how old Kasim is.

12 In a sale the price of a book is reduced by £3. The sale price is £11.

   a) If the original price is £p, write down an equation with p in it.

   b) Solve the equation in part a) to find the original price.

13 An annual subscription to a magazine is £22.50 and costs nine times the monthly price.

   a) If the monthly cost is £m, write down an equation with m in it.

   b) Solve the equation in part a) to find what the monthly price is.

Stage 4

CONTENTS

1 Decimals, fractions and percentages

You should already know

- how to multiply and divide using a calculator
- the value of each digit in a whole number
- that a percentage is a fraction of 100.

ACTIVITY 1

a) Write the following numbers in words.

   (i) 123   **(ii)** 5 496   **(iii)** 91 274   **(iv)** 5 000 007   **(v)** 427 125

b) Write these as numbers using digits.

   (i) four hundred and thirty

   (ii) five thousand, two hundred and twenty-six

   (iii) seventy-five thousand, one hundred and sixteen

   (iv) six million, two thousand and forty

   (v) nine million, seven hundred and twenty-two thousand, four hundred and six.

Decimals

You will have already seen decimal numbers, but here they are looked at in more detail.

A number such as 12·45 has a whole-number part and a decimal part. These are separated by the decimal point which comes after the whole-number part. So a whole number such as 12 is a number that has no decimal part but could have a point at the end.

You should already know that

2145 means 2 thousands, 1 hundred, 4 tens and 5 units

and 1 410 052 means 1 million, 4 hundred thousands, 1 ten thousand, no thousands, no hundreds, 5 tens and 2 units.

In the same way the numbers after the decimal point are tenths ($\frac{1}{10}$), then hundredths ($\frac{1}{100}$), then thousandths ($\frac{1}{1000}$).

EXAMPLE 1

What does the 2 represent in each of these numbers?

a) 12   **b)** 120   **c)** 14·25

d) 3·125   **e)** 41·712

a) 2 units   **b)** 2 tens   **c)** 2 tenths ($\frac{2}{10}$)

d) 2 hundredths ($\frac{2}{100}$)   **e)** 2 thousandths ($\frac{2}{1000}$).

Exam tip

To write a decimal as a fraction, see how many places there are after the decimal point. That is the number of zeros in the denominator (the bottom part) of the fraction.

EXAMPLE 2

Write the meaning of all the digits in these numbers.

a) 2·4   **b)** 321   **c)** 3·64   **d)** 41·915

a) 2 tens and $\frac{4}{10}$

b) 3 hundreds, 2 tens and 1 unit

c) 3 units, $\frac{6}{10}$ and $\frac{4}{100}$

d) 4 hundreds, 1 unit, $\frac{9}{10}$, $\frac{1}{100}$ and $\frac{5}{1000}$.

So 0·45 means 0 units, $\frac{4}{10}$ and $\frac{5}{100}$.

But $\frac{4}{10}$ is the same as $\frac{40}{400}$. So 0·45 can just be written as $\frac{45}{400}$.

In the same way 0·327 means $\frac{3}{10}$, $\frac{2}{100}$ and $\frac{7}{1000}$. But is $\frac{3}{10}$ the same as $\frac{300}{1000}$, and $\frac{2}{100}$ is the same as $\frac{20}{1000}$. So 0·327 can be written as $\frac{327}{1000}$.

EXAMPLE 3

Write these decimals as fractions.

a) 0·3   **b)** 0·25   **c)** 0·312   **d)** 0·041   **e)** 2·3.

a) $\frac{3}{10}$ Only one decimal place, so tenths.

b) $\frac{25}{100}$ Two decimal places, so hundredths.

c) $\frac{312}{1000}$ Three decimal places, so thousandths.

d) $\frac{41}{1000}$ Again three decimal places, but no tenths, so just $\frac{41}{1000}$.

e) $2\frac{3}{10}$ 2 stays the same, and then there are only tenths.

When a number is given as a fraction, it can also be written as a decimal.

EXAMPLE 4

Write as decimals

a) $\frac{7}{10}$ **b)** $\frac{17}{100}$ **c)** $3\frac{105}{1000}$ **d)** $\frac{95}{10\,000}$.

a) 0·7   Just tenths, so one decimal place.

b) 0·17   Hundredths, so two decimal places.

c) 3·105   Three units and thousandths, so three decimal places.

d) 0·0095   Ten thousandths, so four decimal places. Note the two zeros.

EXAMPLE 5

Write these numbers as whole numbers or decimals

a) Four thousand and twenty

b) Two and one tenth

c) Six units and 4 tenths and 1 hundredth

d) Fifty-four and three hundredths.

a) 4020   **No hundreds or units, so zeros for both of those.**

b) 2·1   **Just units and tenths.**

c) 6·41   **Units, tenths and hundredths.**

d) 54·03   **Tens, units and hundredths but not tenths.**

EXERCISE 1.1A

1 What does the 3 represent in each of these numbers?

   a) 53   **b)** 314   **c)** 42·3   **d)** 10·53   **e)** 631

   f) 40·153   **g)** 2·3   **h)** 30 040   **i)** 3 992 110   **j)** 0·003

2 What does the 5 represent in each of these numbers?

   a) 59 176   **b)** 215   **c)** 352·41   **d)** 9·51   **e)** 2·15

   f) 1521·3   **g)** 9·105   **h)** 25 114·2   **i)** 0·005   **j)** 2·1235

3 Write down the meaning of every digit in these numbers.

   a) 41   **b)** 2·3   **c)** 8·04   **d)** 19·12   **e)** 4·615

   f) 15·002   **g)** 6·404   **h)** 146 213   **i)** 900·01   **j)** 63·521

4 Write these decimals as fractions.

   a) 0·9   **b)** 0·87   **c)** 0·654   **d)** 0·121   **e)** 0·301

   f) 1·5   **g)** 0·03   **h)** 3·004   **i)** 0·108   **j)** 0·1205

5 Write these as decimals.

   a) $\frac{1}{10}$ **b)** $\frac{15}{100}$ **c)** $\frac{532}{1000}$ **d)** $\frac{94}{100}$ **e)** $5\frac{7}{10}$

   f) $\frac{104}{1000}$ **g)** $\frac{17}{1000}$ **h)** $42\frac{7}{100}$ **i)** $3\frac{91}{100}$ **j)** $6\frac{3}{1000}$

6 Write these as whole numbers.

   a) seven thousand, two hundred and twenty-five

   b) nine hundred and two

   c) four thousand and twenty

   d) four million, two hundred thousand, five hundred and sixty-four

   e) two thousand and sixteen

Exercise 1.1A cont'd

7 Write these as decimals.

   a) three tenths

   b) four tenths and two hundredths

   c) six tenths, three hundredths and five thousandths

   d) three hundredths

   e) two tenths and nine thousandths

8 Write these as decimals or whole numbers.

   a) two hundred and one

   b) five and four tenths

   c) sixty and two tenths and seven hundredths

   d) eight thousand and two and five hundredths

   e) sixty-four and nine thousandths

EXERCISE 1.1B

1 What does the 6 represent in each of these numbers?

   a) 63   **b)** 316   **c)** 62·3   **d)** 10·6   **e)** 631

   f) 40·163   **g)** 2·56   **h)** 30 640   **i)** 6 443 110   **j)** 0·006

2 What does the 9 represent in each of these numbers?

   a) 59 176   **b)** 295   **c)** 359·41   **d)** 9·51   **e)** 2·19

   f) 1521·9   **g)** 1·129   **h)** 29 114·2   **i)** 0·095   **j)** 6·1295

3 Write down the meaning of every digit in these numbers.

   a) 36   **b)** 8·7   **c)** 4·09   **d)** 26·18   **e)** 1·527

   f) 91·914   **g)** 2·324   **h)** 543 213   **i)** 702·05   **j)** 0·4715

4 Write these decimals as fractions.

   a) 0·2   **b)** 0·75   **c)** 0·548   **d)** 0·213   **e)** 0·031

   f) 6·4   **g)** 2·09   **h)** 5·001   **i)** 0·728   **j)** 0·5905

5 Write these as decimals.

   a) $\frac{2}{10}$ **b)** $\frac{74}{100}$ **c)** $\frac{515}{1000}$ **d)** $\frac{61}{100}$ **e)** $5\frac{3}{10}$

   f) $\frac{123}{1000}$ **g)** $\frac{19}{1000}$ **h)** $12\frac{15}{100}$ **i)** $6\frac{1}{100}$ **j)** $7\frac{23}{1000}$

6 Write these as whole numbers.

   a) ten thousand, four hundred and seventy-four

   b) six hundred and nine

   c) sixty-three thousand and five

   d) eight million, one hundred and two thousand, five hundred and four

   e) seven thousand and one

Exercise 1.1B cont'd

7 Write these as decimals.

a) seven tenths

b) two tenths and nine hundredths

c) seven tenths, two hundredths and five thousandths

d) eight hundredths

e) nine tenths and three thousandths

8 Write these as decimals or whole numbers.

a) three hundred and six

b) three and two tenths

c) two tenths and nine hundredths

d) seven thousand and forty-two and four hundredths

e) three hundred and four and eight thousandths

Putting numbers in order

You already have seen how to put whole numbers in order of size, but here is a reminder.

EXAMPLE 6

Put these numbers in order of size, smallest first.

1421, 512, 3146, 598, 94

Order is 94, 512, 598, 1421, 3146.

The smallest is the number that has only tens and units. Then come the numbers that also have hundreds, starting with the smallest first digit, then the numbers that have thousands, again starting with the smallest first digit.

With decimals the process is similar: look where the first digit is – the nearer it is to the point, the bigger the number is.

EXAMPLE 7

Put these decimals in order of size, smallest first.
0·412, 0·0059, 0·325, 0·046, 0·012, 0·007
Order is 0·0059, 0·007, 0·012, 0·046, 0·325, 0·412.

The smallest are the ones starting with a digit in the third place after the decimal point, and these are in order of size of that digit, no matter how many other digits there are. The next smallest are those with a digit in the second place, and then come those with a digit in the first place.

When the numbers in order include a whole number, just deal with the whole-number part first and then put the decimals in order as needed.

EXAMPLE 8

Put these in order of size, smallest first
3·612, 4·15, 0·273, 0·046, 4·051, 5·105.
Order is 0·046, 0·273, 3·612, 4·051, 4·105, 4·15.

The ones with no whole number are the smallest, ordered as before. Then comes the one with 3 units, followed by those with 4 units, ordered by the decimals.

EXAMPLE 9

Here are 4 digits: 2, 9, 6, 8.

a) What is the smallest whole number you can make using the four digits?

b) What is the largest whole number you can make using the four digits?

a) 2689

The smallest number starts with the smallest digit and then uses them in order of increasing size.

b) 9862

The largest number starts with the largest digit and then uses them in order of decreasing size.

ACTIVITY 2

Write down six whole numbers and swap them with your neighbour. Ask your neighbour to put them in order. See who can do it first!

Now write down six decimal numbers and swap them with your neighbour. Ask your neighbour to put them in order. See who can do it first!

EXERCISE 1.2A

1 Put these whole numbers in order of size, smallest first.

a) 412, 2179, 57, 361, 21, 4215

b) 462, 321, 197, 358, 426, 411

c) 10 425, 5427, 3704, 5821, 6146, 1256

d) 89 125, 39 171, 4621, 59 042, 6317, 9981

e) 120 000, 102 020, 134 050, 104 210, 152 104, 102 002

2 Put these decimals in order of size, smallest first.

a) 0·123, 0·456, 0·231, 0·201, 0·102, 0·114

b) 0·871, 0·561, 0·271, 0·914, 0·832, 0·9

c) 0·01, 0·003, 0·1, 0·056, 0·066, 0·008

d) 0·213, 0·0256, 0·0026, 0·000 141, 0·031, 0·07

e) 0·0404, 0·404, 0·004 04, 0·044, 0·0044, 0·400 04

Exercise 1.2A cont'd

3 Put these numbers in order of size, smallest first.

a) 7·6, 3·42, 1·63, 0·84, 8·9, 4·2

b) 3·12, 3·21, 3·001, 3·102, 3·201, 3·02

c) 1·21, 2·12, 12·1, 121, 0·12, 0·21

d) 53·27, 46·34, 51·96, 51·04, 52, 46·57

e) 7·023, 7·69, 7·015, 7·105, 7·41, 7·14

4 Here are five digits: 6, 1, 3, 4, 2.

a) Write down the smallest whole number that can be made with the five digits, using each digit only once.

b) Write down the largest whole number that can be made with the five digits, using each digit only once.

5 Here are six digits: 2, 5, 0, 4, 6, 9.

a) Write down the smallest whole number that can be made with the six digits, using each digit only once.

b) Write down the largest whole number that can be made with the six digits, using each digit only once.

6 Put these in order, smallest first.

a) $0.23, \frac{21}{100}, \frac{18}{100}, 0.2, 0.17$

b) $0.49, \frac{37}{100}, \frac{56}{100}, 0.50, 0.51$

c) $\frac{91}{100}, 0.81, \frac{8}{10}, 0.9, 0.84$

d) $1\frac{21}{100}, 1\frac{8}{100}, 1.2, 1.17, 1.09$

e) $3.25, 3\frac{2}{10}, 3\frac{18}{100}, 3.204, 3.17$

EXERCISE 1.2B

1 Put these whole numbers in order of size, smallest first.

a) 124, 1792, 75, 631, 12, 415

b) 612, 231, 917, 583, 646, 111

c) 9425, 4257, 7034, 5218, 6641, 1611

d) 86 525, 34 771, 54 621, 9042, 317, 91 981

e) 1 050 403, 1 030 504, 1 020 504, 1 040 501, 1 060 504, 1 010 701.

2 Put these decimals in order of size, smallest first.

a) 0·213, 0·614, 0·317, 0·401, 0·502, 0·514

b) 0·71, 0·51, 0·112, 0·149, 0·2, 0·641

c) 0·05, 0·301, 0·8, 0·516, 0·686, 0·083

d) 0·913, 0·0946, 0·009 16, 0·090 11, 0·091, 0·097

e) 0·03, 0·304, 0·004 304, 0·034, 0·0043, 0·300 04

Exercise 1.2B cont'd

3 Put these numbers in order of size, smallest first.

a) 34·2, 163, 0·84, 8·9, 4·2, 71

b) 5·321, 5·001, 5·0102, 5·0201, 5·02, 5·21

c) 0·01, 12·02, 0·0121, 1·201, 0·0012, 0·21

d) 546·27, 514·3, 15·96, 514·04, 512, 516·57

e) 8·097, 8·79, 8·01, 8·1, 8·04, 8·104

4 Here are five digits: 8, 4, 1, 2, 9.

a) Write down the smallest whole number that can be made with the five digits, using each digit only once.

b) Write down the largest whole number that can be made with the five digits, using each digit only once.

5 Here are six digits: 1, 6, 0, 3, 0, 8.

a) Write down the smallest whole number that can be made with the six digits, using each digit only once.

b) Write down the largest whole number that can be made with the six digits, using each digit only once.

6 Put these in order, smallest first.

a) $0·64, \frac{61}{100}, \frac{58}{100}, 0·62, 0·57$

b) $0·39, \frac{37}{100}, \frac{41}{100}, 0·47, 0·42$

c) $\frac{61}{100}, 0·64, \frac{6}{10}, 0·7, 0·59$

d) $5\frac{21}{100}, 5\frac{3}{10}, 5·2, 5·27, 5·03$

e) $4·75, 4\frac{7}{10}, 4\frac{9}{100}, 4·704, 4·71.$

Fractions and percentages

The only fractions that are included at this stage are halves, quarters, fifths and tenths. You have already worked out these fractions of amounts, both with and without a calculator.

Here is a reminder.

EXAMPLE 10

Work out $\frac{1}{4}$ of 80.

$\frac{1}{4}$ of $80 = \frac{1}{4} \times 80 = 20.$

You also know that a percentage is part of 100, so to find $\frac{1}{4}$ as a percentage, you need to work out $\frac{1}{4}$ of $100 = 25$. So $\frac{1}{4} = 25\%$.

EXAMPLE 11

a) Change $\frac{1}{10}$ to a percentage.

b) Change $\frac{2}{5}$ to a percentage.

a) $\frac{1}{10}$ as a percentage is $\frac{1}{10} \times 100$

$= 10\%$

> **Work out $1 \times 100 \div 10$**

b) $\frac{2}{5}$ as a percentage is $\frac{2}{5} \times 100$.

$= 40\%$

> **Work out $2 \times 100 \div 5$**

To change a percentage to a fraction, you know that the percentage is out of 100, so it can be written as a fraction with the denominator (bottom part) as 100, and then made simpler.

EXAMPLE 12

Change these to fractions

a) 50%

b) 30%

a) $50\% = \frac{50}{100} = \frac{5}{10} = \frac{1}{2}$

> **Divide 50 and 100 by 10 and then by 5.**

b) $30\% = \frac{30}{100} = \frac{3}{10}$

> **Divide 30 and 100 by 10.**

Exam tip

It is useful to know what some simple fractions are as percentages and the reverse.
Especially, remember that
$\frac{1}{2} = 50\%$, $\frac{1}{4} = 25\%$,
$\frac{1}{10} = 10\%$, $\frac{1}{5} = 20\%$.

As you can find a fraction of a quantity, you can also find a percentage of a quantity by changing the percentage to a fraction and working it out.

EXAMPLE 13

Work out

a) 20% of 30

b) 60% of £45.

a) 20% of 30 = $\frac{20}{100} \times 30$ **Work out 20 × 30 ÷ 100.**

$\qquad$ = 6

b) 60% of £45 = £ $\frac{60}{100} \times 45$ **Work out 60 × 45 ÷ 100.**

$\qquad$ = £27

EXERCISE 1.3A

1 Work out

  a) $\frac{1}{5}$ of 40   **b)** $\frac{1}{10}$ of 60   **c)** $\frac{1}{2}$ of 36   **d)** $\frac{1}{4}$ of 24   **e)** $\frac{1}{8}$ of 72.

2 Work out

  a) $\frac{3}{4}$ of 60   **b)** $\frac{3}{10}$ of 90   **c)** $\frac{3}{5}$ of 60   **d)** $\frac{4}{5}$ of 35   **e)** $\frac{7}{10}$ of 80.

3 Change these fractions to percentages.

  a) $\frac{1}{4}$ **b)** $\frac{3}{5}$ **c)** $\frac{3}{10}$ **d)** $\frac{7}{10}$ **e)** $\frac{2}{5}$

4 Change these percentages to fractions.

  a) 40%   **b)** 50%   **c)** 60%   **d)** 75%   **e)** 20%

5 Work out

  a) 10% of 20   **b)** 25% of 64   **c)** 30% of 40   **d)** 40% of 65   **e)** 75% of 24.

6 Half of Form 7A are girls. What percentage is this?

7 Three quarters of the students own a pet. What percentage is this?

8 Jane scored 80% in her exam. What fraction is this?

9 Which is greater, 5% of £800 or 15% of £300? Show your working.

10 Three brothers have agreed to take 10% each of the profits each week from their shop. One week the profits were £400. The eldest one took his 10% and then gave the rest to his younger brother who took his 10% and gave the remainder to the youngest brother who took his 10%. How much did each get. Was this fair?

EXERCISE 1.3B

1 Work out

 a) $\frac{1}{5}$ of 20   **b)** $\frac{1}{10}$ of 30   **c)** $\frac{1}{2}$ of 62   **d)** $\frac{1}{4}$ of 56   **e)** $\frac{1}{8}$ of 40.

2 Work out

 a) $\frac{3}{4}$ of 148   **b)** $\frac{3}{10}$ of 180   **c)** $\frac{2}{5}$ of 145   **d)** $\frac{3}{5}$ of 135   **e)** $\frac{9}{10}$ of 280.

3 Change these fractions to percentages.

 a) $\frac{1}{2}$ **b)** $\frac{3}{4}$ **c)** $\frac{9}{10}$ **d)** $\frac{1}{10}$ **e)** $\frac{4}{5}$

4 Change these percentages to fractions.

 a) 10%   **b)** 30%   **c)** 25%   **d)** 80%   **e)** 90 %

5 Work out

 a) 20% of 150   **b)** 25% of 196   **c)** 5% of 40

 d) 80% of 145   **e)** 75% of 1040.

6 A quarter of students walk to school. What percentage is this?

7 Fiona said she spent one fifth of her time at school doing Maths. What percentage is this?

8 Patrick said that he spent 60% of his time every evening on the internet. What fraction of his time is this?

9 During an evening out with five friends, Barbara paid 10 % of the cost of their meal, which cost £75. Diana paid 25% of their entry into a night club, which cost £30. Who paid more? Show your working.

10 A shop reduces the price of anything which it cannot sell by 10% each week. A boy waits for the price of a fort to come down. The fort is priced at £30 one week. What will be the price the next week? Assuming that it is not sold, work out the price it will be after 2 weeks and 3 weeks. Will it ever be free?

Key ideas

- All terminating decimals can be written as fractions.
- After the decimal point the place values are tenths, then hundredths, then thousandths.
- To change a fraction to a percentage, multiply by 100 and work it out.
- A percentage is a part of 100, so any percentage can be written as a fraction of 100.

2 Coordinates

You should already know

- about basic shapes including rectangles, squares, parallelograms and isosceles and equilateral triangles
- how to plot points in the first quadrant of a grid.

Points in all four quadrants

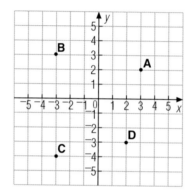

This diagram shows a pair of axes both marked from ⁻5 to +5.

The horizontal axis is called the *x*-axis.

The vertical axis is called the *y*-axis.

They should always be labelled as shown.

The axes divide the grid into four quadrants, which have points A, B, C and D in them.

All points can be defined by coordinates (*x, y*).

The middle point, marked 0, is called the origin and has coordinates (0, 0).

The coordinates of the points on the diagram are

A (3, 2)	3 to the right on the *x*-axis and 2 up on the *y*-axis
B (⁻3, 3)	3 to the left on the *x*-axis and 3 up on the *y*-axis
C (⁻3, ⁻4)	3 to the left on the *x*-axis and 4 down on the *y-axis*
D (2, ⁻3)	2 to the right on the *x*-axis and 3 down on the *y*-axis

Exam tip

When you are drawing axes and marking them, be careful not to miss labelling any line.

Exam tip

When you are reading or plotting a point, the x value always comes first. One way to remember this is to think of an aeroplane taking off. It goes along the ground first and then up.

EXAMPLE 1

Write down the coordinates of the points marked A, B, C and D on the grid.

A $(4, 5)$, B $(^-2, 1)$, C$(^-5, ^-3)$, D$(1, ^-2)$

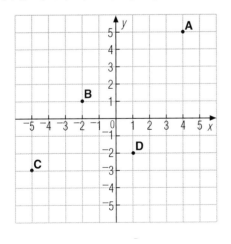

EXAMPLE 2

On squared paper, draw and label axes from $^-5$ to $+5$ for both x and y.

Plot the following points on the graph.

A$(3, 5)$, B$(4, ^-2)$, C$(^-3, 4)$, D$(^-1, ^-5)$

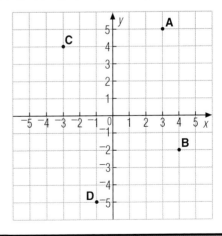

Points on the axes

The points that are most often plotted or read incorrectly are the points that are on either axis.

On this diagram the points A, B, C and D are all on the *x*-axis. Along this axis the values of *x* change but there is no vertical movement so the value of *y* stays at zero.

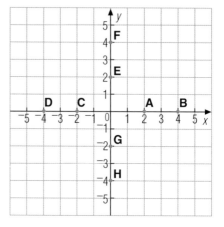

The coordinates are
A(2, 0), B(4, 0), C(‾2, 0), D(‾4, 0).

The points E, F, G, H are all on the *y*-axis where the values of *y* change but there is no horizontal movement so *x* remains at zero.

The coordinates are E(0, 2), F(0, 4), G(0, ‾2), H(0, ‾4).

EXAMPLE 3

On squared paper, draw and label axes from ‾5 to +5 for both *x* and *y*.

Plot the following points on the graph.

A(0, 5)   B(4, 0)   C(0, ‾4)   D(‾1, 0)

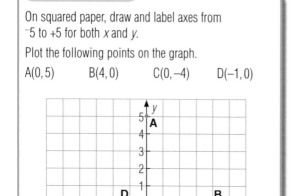

EXERCISE 2.1A

1 Write down the coordinates of the points A to G.

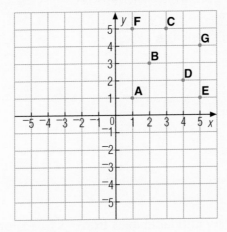

2 On squared paper, draw and label axes from ⁻5 to + 5 for both x and y.
Plot the following points on the graph.

A(3, 1)   B(4, 2)   C(3, 4)   D(1, 5)

3 Write down the coordinates of the points A to G.

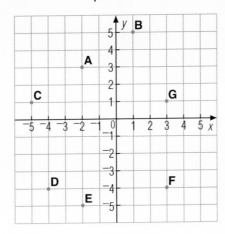

4 On squared paper, draw and label axes from ⁻5 to +5 for both x and y.
Plot the following points on the graph.

A(3, 5)   B(4, ⁻2)   C(⁻3, 4)   D(1, ⁻5)   E(⁻2, ⁻5)   F(⁻4, ⁻1)   G(⁻5, 4)

Exercise 2.1A cont'd

5 Write down the coordinates of the points A to G.

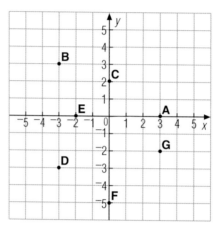

6 On squared paper, draw and label axes from ⁻5 to +5 for both *x* and *y*.
   Plot the following points on the graph
   A(⁻3, 1)   B(4, 0)   C(⁻3, ⁻4)   D(0, ⁻5)   E(⁻2, 0)   F(3, 1)   G(0, 4)

7 In each part of this question draw a grid marked –5 to +5 for both *x* and *y*.
   Join the points to make a letter.
   a) (⁻3, 3), (⁻1, 1), (0, 2), (1, 1), (3, 3)
   b) (⁻3, ⁻3), (⁻3, 3), (0, 1), (3, 3), (3, ⁻3)
   c) (⁻2, ⁻4), (⁻2, 5), (3, 5) and (⁻2, 2), (1, 2)

8 Write a word using coordinates and give the coordinates to a friend to plot
   and work out what the word is.

EXERCISE 2.1B

1 Write down the coordinates of the points A to G.

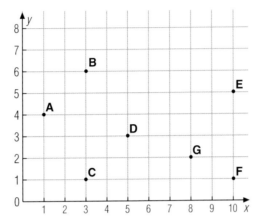

2 On squared paper, draw and label axes from 0 to +8 for both x and y.
Plot the following points on the graph.

A(5, 8)   B(8, 2)   C(7, 4)   D(3, 5)   E(1, 3)   F(5, 1)   G(2, 7)

3 Write down the coordinates of the points A to G.

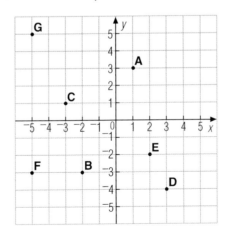

4 On squared paper, draw and label axes from ⁻5 to +5 for both x and y.
Plot the following points on the graph.

A(3,5),   B(⁻4,⁻2),   C(3,⁻4),   D(⁻1,⁻5),   E(⁻5,2),   F(⁻4,5),   G(5,⁻3)

Exercise 2.1B cont'd

5 Write down the coordinates of the points A to G.

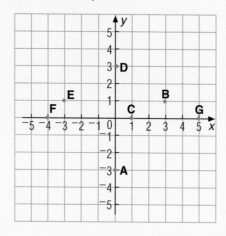

6 On squared paper, draw and label axes from ⁻5 to +5 for both x and y.
Plot the following points on the graph.

A(⁻3, 0)   B(⁻4, ⁻3)   C(0, ⁻4)   D(0, 5)   E(2, 0)   F(5, 2)   G(0, 2)

7 In each part of this question draw a grid marked –5 to +5 for both x and y.
Join the points to make a letter.

a) (⁻2, 4), (⁻2, ⁻3), (3, ⁻3)

b) (⁻3, ⁻4), (2, 4) and (⁻3, 4), (2, ⁻4)

c) (3, ⁻4), (⁻2, ⁻4), (⁻2, 5), (3, 5) and (⁻2, 1), (2, 1)

8 Write 'HOMEWORK' using coordinates.

Shapes can be drawn by plotting points and using simple geometrical facts.

EXAMPLE 4

On squared paper, draw and label axes from
−5 to +5 for both x and y.

a) Plot the following points on the graph.

$\quad$ A(3, 5) $\quad$ B(3, −2) $\quad$ C(−2, −3) $\quad$ D(−2, 4)

b) Join the shape ABCD. What is this shape called?

a)

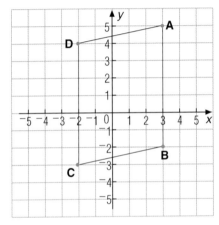

b) A parallelogram.

EXAMPLE 5

On squared paper, draw and label axes from
−5 to +5 for both x and y.

a) Plot the following points on the graph.

$\quad$ (A(3, 3) $\quad$ B(3, −4) $\quad$ C(−5 −4)

b) (i) Mark the point D so that ABCD is a rectangle.

$\quad$ **(ii)** Write down the coordinates of D.

a)

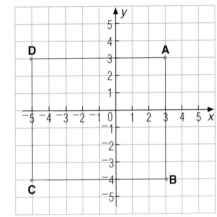

b) (ii) (−5, 3)

EXAMPLE 6

On squared paper, draw and label axes from $^-5$ to $+5$ for both x and y.

a) Plot A($^-3$, 5) and B(5, $^-3$), and join the line AB.

b) (i) Mark the midpoint of AB as C.

   (ii) Write down the coordinates of C.

a) (i)

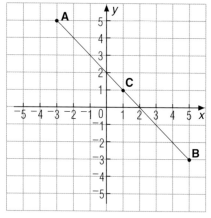

b) (ii) C is (1, 1).

Exam tip

The midpoint of two points can be found without the graph by working out the middle of the two x values, and the middle of the two y values.

ACTIVITY 1

Complete this table

Pair	First point		Second point		Midpoint	
	x	y	x	y	x	y
a)	2	3	6	9		
b)	3	1	7	1		
c)	$^-1$	4	5	2		
d)	3	5	5	$^-1$		
e)	$^-2$	$^-5$	4	$^-1$		

EXERCISE 2.2A

1 On squared paper, draw and label axes from ⁻5 to +5 for both x and y.
   a) Plot the following points on the graph.
   A(3, ⁻3)   B(⁻4, ⁻1)   C(⁻2, 3)   D(1, 2)   E(5, ⁻1)
   b) Join the shape ABCDE. What is the name of this shape?

2 On squared paper, draw and label axes from ⁻5 to +5 for x and y.
   a) On the graph
      (i) plot A(3, 5) and B(⁻4, 5) and join the line AB.
      (ii) plot C(⁻2, ⁻3) and D(⁻2, 5) and join the line CD.
   b) What can you say about the lines AB and CD?

3 On squared paper, draw and label axes from –5 to +5 for both x and y.
   a) Plot the following points on the graph
      A(1, ⁻3)   B(2, 4)   C(⁻3, 2)   D(⁻4, ⁻5)
   b) Join the shape ABCD. What is this shape called?

4 On squared paper, draw and label axes from ⁻5 to +5 for both x and y.
   a) Plot the following points on the graph.
      A(2, 5)   B(5, 2)   C(2, ⁻1)
   b) **(i)** Mark the point D on the graph so that ABCD is a square.
      (ii) Write down the coordinates of D.

5 On squared paper, draw and label axes from ⁻5 to +5 for both x and y.
   a) Plot A(3, 5) and B(⁻5, ⁻1), on the graph.
   b) **(i)** Join AB and mark the midpoint of AB as C.
      (ii) Write down the coordinates of C.

6 Mark axes from ⁻5 to +5 for both x and y. Plot the points (1, 2) and (3, 2). These are two corners of a square. Find the other two corners. Is there more than one solution?

Chapter 2 *Coordinates*

EXERCISE 2.2B

1 On squared paper, draw and label axes from ⁻5 to +5 for both x and y.

    a) Plot the following points on the graph.

    A(3, ⁻3)   B(⁻1, 1),   D(⁻5, ⁻3)

    b) Join the triangle ABC. What is the special name of this triangle?

2 On squared paper, draw and label axes from ⁻5 to +5 for both x and y.

    a) Plot the following points on the graph.

    A(3, 5)   B(⁻2, 5)   C(⁻2, ⁻3)   D(3, ⁻3)

    b) Join the shape ABCD. What is this shape called?

3 On squared paper, draw and label axes from ⁻5 to +5 for both x and y.

    a) Plot the following points on the graph.

    A(0, ⁻3)   B(4, 1)   C(0, 5)   D(⁻4, 1)

    b) Join the shape ABCD. What is this shape called?

4 On squared paper, draw and label axes from ⁻5 to +5 for both x and y.

    a) Plot the following points on the graph.

    A(2, 5)   B(⁻5, 5)   C(⁻5, ⁻5)

    b) **(i)** Mark the point D on the graph so that ABCD is a rectangle.

          (ii) Write down the coordinates of D.

5 On squared paper, draw and label axes from ⁻5 to +5 for both x and y.

    a) Plot A(⁻3, 5) and B(3, 1), on the graph.

    b) **(i)** Mark the midpoint of AB as C

          (ii) Write down the coordinates of C.

6 Mark axes from ⁻10 to +10 for both x and y. Plot the points (2, 1) and (3, 6). These are two corners of a square. Find the other two corners. Is there more than one solution?

Key ideas

- On a graph the horizontal axis is the x-axis and the vertical axis is the y-axis.
- Coordinates are always given as (x, y).
- On the x-axis the y coordinate is 0 and on the y-axis the x coordinate is 0.
- The midpoint of the line joining the points (a, b) and (c, d) is $(\frac{a+c}{2}, \frac{b+d}{2})$

3 Area and perimeter of triangles and composite shapes

You should already know

- the meaning of the terms perimeter and area
- how to find the area of a rectangle
- that areas are measured in square units
- that perimeters are measured in linear units
- how to plot points on a graph.

In this chapter the diagrams are not to scale, except when they are on grids.

Area of a triangle

ACTIVITY 1

Plots these points on squared paper and join them up to make triangles.

a) (2, 1), (2, 5), (4, 1)   **b)** (1, 1), (5, 1), (5, 3)

c) (⁻3, ⁻3), (4, ⁻3), (2, 4)   **d)** (⁻5, ⁻4), (⁻4, 3), (3, ⁻4)

e) (⁻5, ⁻2), (5, ⁻2), (0, 4)

Copy the table and fill it in by measuring the base, the height and, by counting squares, the area of the triangles.

Triangle	Base	Height	Area
a)			
b)			
c)			
d)			
e)			

Write down anything you notice.

You should already have learnt how to find the area of a right-angled triangle. This is now extended to all triangles.

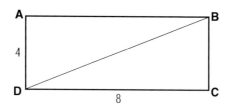

In this diagram the lengths are in centimetres.

The area of the rectangle is $8 \times 4 = 32\,\text{cm}^2$.

The area of triangle DBC is half of the area of the rectangle so it is $16\,\text{cm}^2$.

This can be worked out as $\frac{1}{2} \times 8 \times 4 = 16\,\text{cm}^2$.

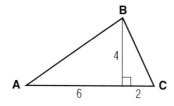

Triangle ABC is not right-angled but it can be split into two right-angled triangles.

The area of the left-hand triangle is $\frac{1}{2} \times 6 \times 4 = 12\,\text{cm}^2$.

The area of the right-hand triangle is $\frac{1}{2} \times 2 \times 4 = 4\,\text{cm}^2$.

Therefore the full area of the triangle is $12 + 4 = 16\,\text{cm}^2$.

This is the same as $\frac{1}{2} \times 8 \times 4 = 16\,\text{cm}^2$.

> **This shows that the area of any triangle can be found as**
>
> $\qquad \frac{1}{2} \times$ **base** $\times$ **perpendicular height**
>
> **or   Area of triangle** $= \frac{1}{2} \times b \times h$

Chapter 3   *Area and perimeter of triangles and composite shapes*

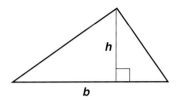 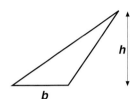

This is true for all triangles.

When you are using the formula, you can use any side of the triangle as the base providing you use the perpendicular height that goes with it.

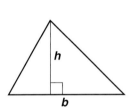 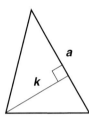 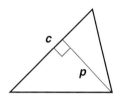

Area = $\frac{1}{2} \times b \times h$ or area = $\frac{1}{2} \times a \times k$ or area = $\frac{1}{2} \times c \times p$.

EXAMPLE 1

Find the area of these triangles.

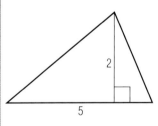 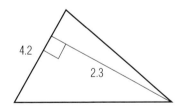

a) Area = $\frac{1}{2} \times 5 \times 2 = 5\,\text{cm}^2$ **b)** Area = $\frac{1}{2} \times 4{\cdot}2 \times 2{\cdot}3 = 4{\cdot}83\,\text{cm}^2$

EXAMPLE 2

a) On squared paper, draw a triangle with vertices A(1, 2), B(1, 6) and C(5, 3).

b) Find the area of the triangle.

a)

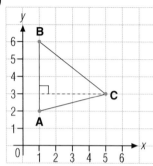

b) Area = $\frac{1}{2} \times 4 \times 4 = 8$ squares.

In this case AB is used as the base, and the distance to C from AB as the height.

EXERCISE 3.1A

1 Find the area of these triangles. All lengths are in centimetres.

a)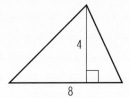

b)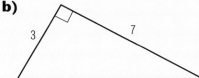

c)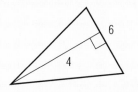

d)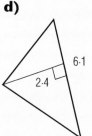

e)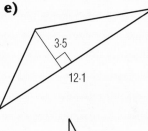

f)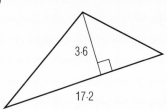

g)

h)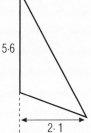

2 The vertices of a triangle are A(1, 3), B(5, 3) and C(2, 7).

  a) On squared paper, draw the triangle.

  b) Work out its area.

3 The vertices of a triangle are A(3, 1), B(8, 1) and C(3, 7).

  a) On squared paper, draw the triangle.

  b) Work out its area.

4 The vertices of a triangle are A(8, 3), B(8, 6) and C(1, 4).

  a) On squared paper, draw the triangle.

  b) Work out its area.

5 The vertices of a triangle are A(1,1), B(1, 5) and C(5, 7).

  a) On squared paper, draw the triangle.

  b) Work out its area.

6 On squared paper, draw some different triangles with an area of 8 squares.

EXERCISE 3.1B

1 Find the area of these triangles. All lengths are in centimetres.

a)

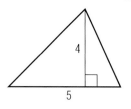

4
5

b)

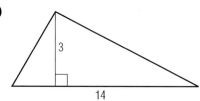

3
14

c)

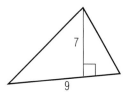

7
9

d)

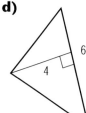

6
4

e)

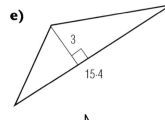

3
15·4

f)

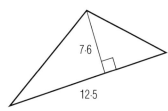

7·6
12·5

g)

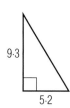

9·3
5·2

h)

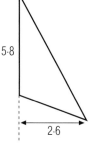

5·8
2·6

2 The vertices of a triangle are A(1, 2), B(5, 2) and C(2, 8).

  a) On squared paper, draw the triangle.

  b) Work out its area.

3 The vertices of a triangle are A(3, 4), B(8, 4) and C(3, 1).

  a) On squared paper, draw the triangle.

  b) Work out its area.

4 The vertices of a triangle are A(1, 3), B(1, 6) and C(5, 4).

  a) On squared paper, draw the triangle.

  b) Work out its area.

5 The vertices of a triangle are A(1, 1), B(6, 5) and C(5, 1).

  a) On squared paper, draw the triangle.

  b) Work out its area.

6 On squared paper, draw some different triangles with an area of 6 squares.

Area and perimeter of shapes made up of rectangles and triangles

The perimeter of a shape is the distance all the way round the outside of the shape.

EXAMPLE 3

Work out the perimeter of these shapes. All lengths are in centimetres.

a)

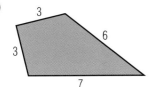

b)

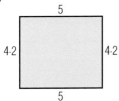

c)

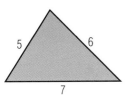

a) Perimeter = 4·2 + 5 + 4·2 + 5   = 18·4 cm.

b) Perimeter = 3 + 3 + 6 + 7   = 19 cm.

c) Perimeter = 5 + 6 + 7   = 18 cm.

A way to find the area of many shapes is to split them up into rectangles and triangles.

EXAMPLE 4

Work out **(i)** the perimeter and **(ii)** the area of these shapes. All lengths are in centimetres.

a)

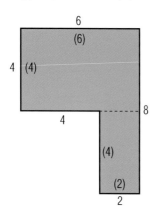

b)

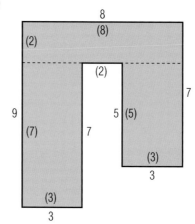

The lengths marked in brackets were not all given in the question, but are worked out. The dotted lines have been added as part of the answer.

a) **(i)** The perimeter of the shape is $6 + 8 + 2 + 4 + 4 + 4 = 28$ cm.

   (ii) The area is $6 \times 4 + 2 \times 4 = 24 + 8 = 32$ cm^2.

The shape has been split into two rectangles by a horizontal dotted line. It could have been split in a different way by a vertical line.

b) **(ii)** The perimeter of the shape is $9 + 8 + 7 + 3 + 5 + 2 + 7 + 3 = 44$ cm.

   (ii) The area is $8 \times 2 + 7 \times 3 + 5 \times 3 = 16 + 21 + 15 = 52$ cm^2.

The shape has been split into three rectangles.

Exam tip

A common error is to split the shape correctly but then multiply the wrong numbers to get the area. In the example 4(b) a possible error for the second rectangle is to work out 9×3 instead of 7×3.

EXAMPLE 5

Work out the areas of these shapes.

a)

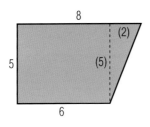

b)

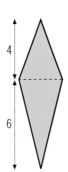

a) Area $= 5 \times 6 + \frac{1}{2} \times 5 \times 2 = 30 + 5 = 35\,cm^2$.

This has been split by the vertical dashed line into a rectangle and a triangle.

b) Area $= \frac{1}{2} \times 4 \times 3 + \frac{1}{2} \times 6 \times 3 = 6 + 9 = 15\,cm^2$.

This has been split by the horizontal line into two triangles.

EXAMPLE 6

a) On squared paper plot the points A(1, 3), B(2, 6), C(5, 5), D(6, 2), E(3, 1).
Join them up to make the pentagon ABCDE.

b) Find the area of the pentagon by splitting it into rectangles and triangles.

a)

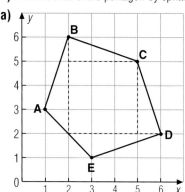

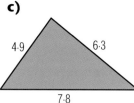

Exam tip

When splitting shapes on a grid, try to make sure that all triangles have an exact number of squares for the base and the height.

b) Area $= 3 \times 3 + \frac{1}{2} \times 4 \times 1 + \frac{1}{2} \times 3 \times 1 + \frac{1}{2} \times 3 \times 1 + \frac{1}{2} \times 4 \times 1$
$= 9 + 2 + 1\cdot5 + 1\cdot5 + 2 = 16$ squares

The pentagon has been split into one rectangle and four triangles.
This is not the only way it could be split.

EXERCISE 3.2A

1 Find the perimeter of these shapes. All lengths are in centimetres.

a)

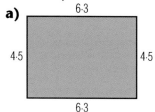

6·3
4·5   4·5
6·3

b)

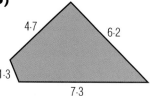

4·7   6·2
1·3
7·3

c)

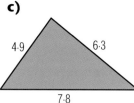

4·9   6·3
7·8

d)

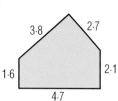

3·8   2·7
1·6   2·1
4·7

e)

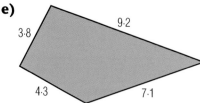

3·8   9·2
4·3   7·1

Exercise 3.2A cont'd

2 Work out **(i)** the perimeter and **(ii)** the area of these shapes. All lengths are in centimetres.

a)

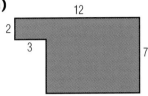

b)

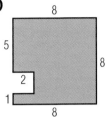

c)

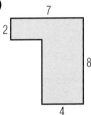

d)

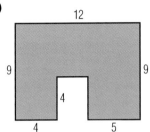

e)

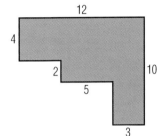

3 Work out the area of these shapes.

a)

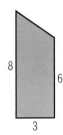

b)

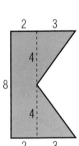

c)

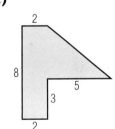

d)

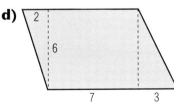

e)

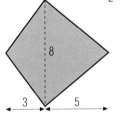

4 a) On squared paper, plot the points A(2, 1), B(3, 5), C(6, 5), D(6, 1). Join them to make the quadrilateral ABCD.

b) Split the shape into triangles and rectangles and find its area.

Exercise 3.2A cont'd

5 **a)** On squared paper, plot the points A(4, 2), B(2, 6), C(4, 8), D(6, 6). Join them to make the quadrilateral ABCD.

b) Split the shape into triangles and rectangles and find its area.

6 **a)** On squared paper, plot the points A(1, 1), B(4, 5), C(7, 5), D(5, 1). Join them to make the quadrilateral ABCD.

b) Split the shape into triangles and rectangles and find its area.

7 **a)** On squared paper, plot the points A(1, 1), B(1, 4), C(3, 6), D(5, 4), E(5, 1). Join them to make the pentagon ABCDE.

b) Split the shape into triangles and rectangles and find its area.

8 **a)** On squared paper, plot the points A(1, 4), B(3, 5), C(4, 7), D(5, 5), E(7, 4), F(5, 3), G(4, 1), H(3, 3). Join them to make the polygon ABCDEFGH.

b) Split the shape into triangles and rectangles and find its area.

9 **a)** On squared paper, plot the points A(1, 1), B(3, 4), C(5, 4), D(6, 2), E(5, 1). Join them to make the pentagon ABCDE.

b) Split the shape into triangles and rectangles and find its area.

10 **a)** On squared paper, plot the points A(2, 2), B(2, 5), C(5, 7), D(8, 5), E(8, 2), F(5, 4). Join them to make the hexagon ABCDEF.

b) Split the shape into triangles and rectangles and find its area.

EXERCISE 3.2B

1 Find the perimeter of these shapes. All lengths are in centimetres.

a)

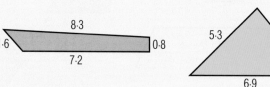

b)

c)

d)

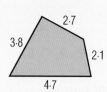

e)

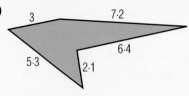

Exercise 3.2B cont'd

2 Work out **(i)** the perimeter and **(ii)** the area of these shapes. All lengths are in centimetres.

a)
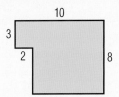

b)

c)
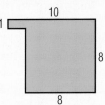

d)
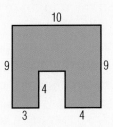

e)
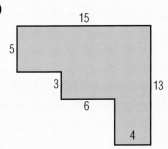

3 Work out the area of these shapes.

a)
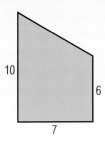

b)
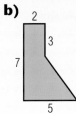

c)
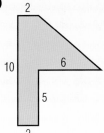

d)
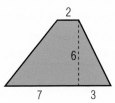

e)
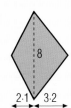

Chapter 3   *Area and perimeter of triangles and composite shapes*

Exercise 3.2B cont'd

4 a) On squared paper, plot the points A(2, 1), B(2, 5), C(6, 5), D(4, 1). Join them to make the quadrilateral ABCD.

b) Split the shape into triangles and rectangles and find its area.

5 a) On squared paper, plot the points, A(1, 2), B(2, 6), C(4, 8), D(6, 6). Join them to make the quadrilateral ABCD.

b) Split the shape into triangles and rectangles and find its area.

6 a) On squared paper, plot the points A(1, 2), B(5, 4), C(6, 2), D(5, 1). Join them to make the quadrilateral ABCD.

b) Split the shape into triangles and rectangles and find its area.

7 a) On squared paper, plot the points A(2, 3), B(4, 5), C(6, 3), D(6, 1), E(4, 1). Join them to make the pentagon ABCDE.

b) Split the shape into triangles and rectangles and find its area.

8 a) On squared paper, plot the points A(4, 6), B(7, 4), C(7, 2), D(5, 1), E(3, 1), F(1, 2), G(1, 4). Join them to make the polygon ABCDEFG.

b) Split the shape into triangles and rectangles and find its area.

9 a) On squared paper, plot the points A(1, 2), B(2, 4), C(5, 4), D(5, 1), F(2, 1). Join them to make the pentagon ABCDE.

b) Split the shape into triangles and rectangles and find its area.

10 a) On squared paper, plot the points A(1, 5), B(3, 7), C(7, 7), D(9, 5), E(7, 2), F(2, 3). Join them to make the hexagon ABCDEF.

b) Split the shape into triangles and rectangles and find its area.

Key ideas

● **The area of a triangle is $\frac{1}{2} \times$ base $\times$ perpendicular height.**

4 Problems involving decimals

You should already know

- how to use a calculator to add, subtract, multiply and divide whole numbers and decimals
- how to add and subtract whole numbers and decimals without a calculator
- how to multiply and divide a decimal by an integer without a calculator
- how to work with hours and minutes
- how to find perimeters and areas of rectangles.

Exam tip

Getting the right answer is especially important in practical problems. You need ways of checking whether your answer is correct.

ACTIVITY 1

Make sure you can do these without a calculator.

1 4·64 + 3·21	**2** 5·91 + 3·75	**3** 4·65 − 2·14	**4** 6·32 + 2·17	**5** 9 − 3·16
6 4 × 3·21	**7** 5·14 × 6	**8** 0·24 × 9	**9** 3·24 × 8	**10** 6·14 × 3
11 8·4 ÷ 2	**12** 14·7 ÷3	**13** 2·64 ÷ 4	**14** 8·6 ÷ 5	**15** 18·6 ÷ 6

16 1 hour 14 minutes + 2 hours 25 minutes   **17** 2 hours 45 minutes + 30 minutes

18 3 hours 51 minutes + 4 hours 10 minutes   **19** 2 hours 32 minutes + 1 hour 44 minutes

20 3 hours 27 minutes + 1 hour 46 minutes.

ACTIVITY 2

Work these out using your calculator.

1 4.6×3 **2** 5.1×3 **3** 4.6×3.2 **4** $7.15 + 6.234$ **5** $9000 - 3217$

6 $47.5 \div 2.5$ **7** $0.198 \div 3$ **8** $46.251 - 3.842 + 6.145$ **9** $2.841 \times 3.2 \div 2.4$

10 $62.47 \times 9.3 - 4.61 \times 2.62$

Using information to solve problems

Mathematical information is presented in many ways. TV programme schedules, mileage charts, timetables and holiday booking information are all examples of practical situations in which you may need to use mathematics.

Often, there is far more information than you need to use, so don't spend time trying to take it all in.

a) Have a quick look at the information given to see what it is about and how it is organised.

b) Then read the question carefully.

c) Then go back to the information to find out what you need.

EXAMPLE 1

How far is it from Carlisle to Glasgow?

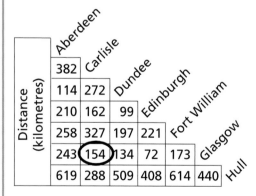

The distance is 154 km.

Exam tip

When information is in a table, use the row and column headings to help you. Check twice that you have used the correct row and column.

Look down the Carlisle column and across the Glasgow row.

The entry you need has been circled in the chart.

EXAMPLE 2

The table shows some postage costs.

Weight up to	First class	Second class
60 g	£0.27	£0.19
100 g	£0.41	£0.33
150 g	£0.47	£0.44
200 g	£0.57	£0.54
250 g	£0.72	£0.66
300 g	£0.84	£0.76
350 g	£0.96	£0.87
400 g	£1.24	£1.00

a) Katie had an item to post. It weighed 320 g. How much did it cost to post this first class?

b) How much cheaper would it be to post an item weighing 130 g second class instead of first class?

a) The cost was £1.09. **For this item, the row for weight up to 350 g is needed.**

b) The difference is 47p – 44p = 3p. **Use the 150 g row.**

ACTIVITY 3

Obtain an up-to-date card of postage costs and use it to work out the cost of sending a letter weighing

a) 40 g, first class **b)** 70 g, second class
c) 120 g, first class **d)** 380 g, second class
e) 95 g, first class.

EXAMPLE 3

Slade Museum had this offer:

MUSEUM

PRICES
Adluts £4.50 Children £2.50
Senior Citizens £2.50
1 child free with every full
paying adult.

Mrs Barnes took her three children and her mother to this museum.
Her mother is a senior citizen. How much did they have to pay altogether?

They had to pay for one adult, two children and 1 senior citizen.

This cost 1 × £4.25 + 3 × £2.50 = £11.75.

EXERCISE 4.1A

1 Use the postage chart in Example 2 to find the cost of posting

   a) a 270 g letter second class
   b) a 395 g letter first class.

2 Pete watched a film on TV. It started at 1.40 p.m. and was 1 hour 45 minutes long. At what time did it end?

3 Look at this distance chart.

Distance in miles

Exeter				
152	Guildford			
154	67	Oxford		
109	49	66	Southampton	
34	131	121	93	Taunton

   a) Amy travels from Guildford to Southampton and then from Southampton to Exeter.

   How many miles does she travel?

   b) On her return journey she drives directly to Guildford from Exeter. How many miles less is this than her journey from Guildford to Exeter?

4 Use the chart in question 3 to find how much further it is to drive from Oxford to Exeter than from Oxford to Taunton.

5 Here were the programmes on BBC1 one afternoon:

1.45	Neighbours
2.05	Quincey
2.55	Through the Keyhole
3.25	Children's BBC
5.35	Neighbours

   a) Sarah watched Quincey. How long was this programme?

   b) Tommy watched all of Children's BBC. How long was this?

6 The first class postage cost of items over 1000 g in April 2000 was given as '£3.32 plus 81p for each 250 g or part thereof'.

   How much did it cost to post a first class parcel weighing 1130 g?

7

GALICIA Hotel Sangeno

All prices £s per person from Heathrow

Departures on or between	7 nights	14 nights
Holiday code	**STO30RQ**	**STO31RQ**
Apr 18–May 1	399	569
May 2–15	429	599
May 16–29	449	639
May 30–Jun 16	479	679
Discounts if you do not need our travel insurance	30	40

Mr and Mrs Bryant want to book a seven-night holiday at the Hotel Sangeno, departing from Heathrow on 20th May. They already have other travel insurance.

   a) What holiday code should they use on their booking form?

   b) How much do they need to pay?

Exercise 4.1A cont'd

8 A cinema had a half-price seat offer for children during the holidays. The full price for a seat was £4.20. Mr. Lewis took five children to the cinema. How much did it cost altogether for their seats?

9 Sam and Jane want to order some of these trousers. They want one red pair in size 14 and two navy pairs in size 20. Copy and complete the order form.

Trousers	Size	QTY	Colour	Price	Total
10, 12, 14, 16, 18 20, 22, 24, 26				£14.99 £16.99	
			add postage and packing	£1.95	
			TOTAL		

10 A return car ferry booking cost £259 in August, including two nights' overnight accommodation for two people in hotels in France. Extra nights cost £42 per night for two people. To travel to and from the South of France, Jim and Vita Mennon wanted a return car ferry crossing and six nights' accommodation altogether. How much did they pay for this booking?

EXERCISE 4.1B

1 Use the postage chart in Example 2 to find the cost of posting

   a) a 90 g letter second class

   b) a 185 g letter first class.

2 An international football match commentary on radio started at 7.55 p.m. and ended at 10 p.m. How long was this programme?

3 Look at this distance chart.

Distance in (miles)

Birmingham
116	Leeds				
99	74	Liverpool			
172	63	144	Middlesborough		
159	172	240	223	Norwich	
129	24	102	50	181	York

a) How many miles is it from Leeds to York?

b) How much further away is Middlesbrough from Norwich than it is from Birmingham?

4 Use the chart in question 3.

   a) Mr Jones drives one day from Birmingham to Liverpool, then from Liverpool to York.

   How long is his journey?

   b) The next day he drives from York to Norwich and from there back to Birmingham.

   How many miles more does he drive on the second day than the first?

Exercise 4.1B cont'd

5 **FRANCE CAR HIRE**
Prices are per car in £s per day

Number of days		Seats	3 to 6	7 to 13	14+
Group A	Renault Twingo or similar	4	25	22	21
Group B	Renault Clio 1·2 or similar	4	30	26	25
Group C	Renault Mégane 1·4 A/C or similar	4 to 5	34	29	27
Group D	Renault Laguna 1·8 A/C or similar	4 to 5	40	35	33

The Brown family want to hire a Renault Mégane for a 17-day holiday. How much will the car hire cost from France Car Hire?

6 The White family paid £234 for a nine-day booking from France Car Hire. Use the table in question 3 to find what group the car they hired was in.

7 Here were the children's TV programmes one morning.

7.00	Mr Benn	8.50	Goosebumps
7.15	Playdays	9.35	Little Bear
7.35	Busy World	10.00	Teletubbies
8.00	Dastardly and Muttley	10.30	Tweenies
8.20	Against All Odds	[10.50 end]	

Bill watched 'Busy World' and 'Dastardly and Muttley'. How long did he watch for?

8 What was the longest of the programmes listed in question 7, and how long was it?

9 The first class postage cost of items over 1000 g in April 2000 was given as '£3.32 plus 81p for each 250 g or part thereof'. How much did it cost to post a first class parcel weighing 1450 g?

10 The charge for an advertisement in the local paper is £2.50, plus 16p for each word.

Steve put a 23-word advert in the paper. How much did he pay?

More problems using calculators

When you are solving some problems, you first of all need to decide whether to add, subtract, multiply or divide before you can use your calculator.

EXAMPLE 4

Stephen had a five pound note and bought six tins of beans. He received £3.26 change.
How much did each tin cost?

Amount spent on beans = £5 − £3.26 = £1.74
or 174 pence

> **You first need to subtract £3.26 from £5 to find the amount spent.**

Cost of one tin = 174 ÷ 6 = 29 pence

> **Then you needed to divide the amount spent by 6.**

EXAMPLE 5

Glenda wants to build a fence 17·2 metres long.
The fencing is sold in 1·5-metre lengths.
a) How many lengths will she need to buy?
b) How much fencing will she have left over?

a) 17·2 ÷ 1·5 = 11·47
   So she must buy 12 lengths.

> **Divide 17·2 by 1·5, but she cannot buy fractions of a length.**

b) 12 × 1·5 = 18
   18 − 17·2 = 0·8 metres
   Amount left is 0·8 metres.

> **To find how much is left over, first multiply 12 by 1·5 and then subtract 17·2.**

EXERCISE 4.2A

1 Cora buys five loaves at 32 pence each. How much does she spend?

2 A lorry can carry 800 kg. How many sacks, each weighing 50 kg, can it carry?

3 A bottle holds 2000 ml of liquid. How many glasses, each holding 150 ml, can be filled from the bottle? How much is left over?

4 Alan buys three tins of spaghetti at 31 pence each and two packets of soup at 57 pence each.

How much does he spend altogether?

5 Tony wants a rectangular piece of hardboard 25·4 cm by 36·7 cm. He has a piece 30 cm by 48 cm. How much must he cut off each side?

6 Lyn buys 84 jelly sweets to share equally between her four children.

How many do they get each?

7 Five friends had a meal together which cost £48.50. They shared the bill between them.

How much did each pay?

8 The length of the swimming pool at Heeley baths is 25 metres. Jason swam 1400 metres in one session. How many lengths was this?

9 Sebastian bought eight tins of paint at £3.45 each. How much change did he get from £30?

10 At the toddlers' group, adults pay 35p each plus 75p for each child. On Tuesday 17 October there were 18 adults and 27 children. How much was taken altogether?

Exercise 4.2A cont'd

11 To go to the theatre Freda bought one adult ticket at £15.50 and three child tickets. She spent £40.25 altogether. How much did each child ticket cost?

12 Cedric was assembling small items, which took him 20 minutes each. One day he started work at 9 a.m. and finished at 5.30 p.m. He had breaks of 1 hour and 30 minutes in total during the day. How many items did he assemble?

13 A rectangle is 8·315 cm long and 4·521 cm wide.

   a) How much bigger is the length than the width?

   b) What is the perimeter of the rectangle?

14 David and Shirley both worked out a question using a calculator. David's answer was 4·217, Shirley's answer was 4·127. Who's answer was bigger and by how much?

15 In a race Carl's time was 22·751 seconds and Linford's time was 21·963 seconds.

   Who was quicker and by how much?

EXERCISE 4.2B

1 Jon paid for himself and four friends to enter a museum. The total cost was £32.50. How much did it cost for each one?

2 Paint is sold in 2·5-litre cans and Andy needs 15 litres to paint his house. How many tins should he buy?

3 A bath holds 50 litres of water. It takes 5 seconds to pour in 1 litre.

   a) How many seconds does it take to fill the bath?

   b) How many minutes and seconds does it take to fill the bath? (There are 60 seconds in one minute.)

Exercise 4.2B cont'd

4 At the gym, Paul rowed 2100 metres, cycled 3000 metres and walked 1750 metres on the various machines. What distance did he cover in total?

5 Marc, his wife and two children all went on a car ferry with their car. It cost £118 for the car, £28 for each adult and £15 for each child. What did it cost him altogether?

6 On a seven-day touring holiday Pam and Daryl travelled 1760 miles altogether. The distances they travelled on each of the first six days were 284 miles, 312 miles, 124 miles, 215 miles, 191 miles and 319 miles. How far did they travel on the last day?

7 At the fairground Graham went on the dodgems twice, the carousel once and the roller coaster four times. For one ride it cost £1.50 on the dodgems, £1.00 on the carousel and £2.25 on the roller coaster. How much did he spend altogether?

8 To tie up his roses, Carlos uses 0·8 m of string for each rose. He had a 10 m ball of string to start with and ended with 3·6 m. How many roses did he tie up?

9 A rugby pack of eight students weighs 684 kg in total. The weights of seven of the students are 72 kg, 84 kg, 91 kg, 81 kg, 75 kg, 96 kg, and 98 kg. What is the weight of the eighth student.

10 Joanne bought eight first class stamps at 27 pence each and six second class stamps. She paid with a £5 note and received £1.70 change. How much did each second class stamp cost?

Exercise 4.2B cont'd

11 To make a glass of orange squash, Ada uses 30 ml of concentrated orange. She bought a bottle that contained 2 litres or 2000 ml of concentrated orange. After making 43 glasses of orange, how much concentrated orange did she have left?

12 Abigail is saving for her holiday. She earns £12.75 a week from her paper round and her dad gives her £8 a week spending money. She spends £11.20 a week on various items and saves the rest. How much will she have saved in 15 weeks?

13 Four friends won some money. They worked out how much each would receive if they shared it equally. It came to £417.325 each. How much did they win altogether?

14 The masses of three parcels were 2·356 kg, 4·912 kg and 2·674 kg.

   a) What was the difference between the mass of the heaviest and the lightest.

   b) What was the total mass of all three.

15 To ring a person in Britain costs £0.03 per minute.

   a) How much is this per second?

   There is also a connection charge of £0.035 for every call. Gracie phoned Jessie and was on the phone for 48 seconds.

   b) How much did this cost in total?

Key ideas

● When using information to solve problems have a quick look at it to see what it is about and how it is organised, read the question carefully and then go back to the information and see what you need.

● When a problem has a number of steps, work out which operations to do and in which order, then do them carefully, writing down your intermediate results.

A1 Revision exercise

1 What does 3 represent in each of these numbers?

    a) 321   **b)** 2·31

    c) 0·003   **d)** 31462

2 Put these numbers in order of size, smallest first.

    3·61, 3·016, 3·621, 3·106, 3·126

3 Work out

    a) 50% of 48   **b)** $\frac{3}{10}$ of 60.

4 Write as a fraction.

    a) 0·3   **b)** 0·07

    c) 25%

5 On squared paper, draw and label axes from ⁻5 to + 5 for both x and y.

    a) Plot the following points.
    A(⁻5, 1), B(⁻1, 4), C(5, 1), D(1, ⁻2)
    and join ABCD.

    b) Give the special name for the shape ABCD.

    c) Find the coordinates of the midpoint of BD.

6 Find the area of these shapes. All lengths are in centimetres.

    a)

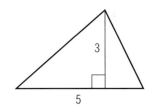

    b)

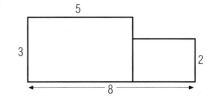

7 Find the perimeter of these shapes. All the lengths are in centimetres.

    a)

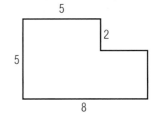

    b)

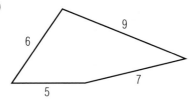

8 Here is a table showing the cost of car hire (in £) for one week in Canada.

canada		nov–mar	apr–Jun& 16 sep–oct	jul–15 sep
ecar*	chevrolet metro 2dr auto a/c	169	169	185
ccar	chervrolet cavalier 2dr auto a/c	182	189	209
idar	pontiac grand am 4dr auto a/c	199	215	235
scar	monte carlo 2dr auto a/c	229	229	265
idar	cadillac de ville 4dr auto a/c	269	269	289
fvar	minivan 7 seats auto a/c	272	289	299
ifar	explorer 2dr 4×4 auto a/c	289	289	299

Canada: includes free one way rentals between Vancouver and Calgary, Toronto and Montreal, Vancouver and Edmonton, Edmonton to Calgary.
* a/c not available at all locations.

How much does it cost to hire a minivan 7 seats auto a/c for two weeks in December?

9 David paid for three tins of paint at £4.75 each with a £20 note. How much change did he get?

10 Mira took part in a sponsored walk. She walked 12 kilometres. This is a copy of her sponsor card. How much did she raise altogether?

Name	Amount per km	Total amount
Dave	10p	
Mary	5p	
Dawn	20p	
Mrs Shepherd	50p	
Mr Shepherd	50p	
Mrs Green	20p	
Mr Spencer	25p	
Grant	10p	

5 Averages and range

You should already know

- how to find the mean, median and mode for a set of discrete data
- how to find the range for a set of discrete data.

This chapter looks at using the measures of average and range to compare different distributions.

ACTIVITY 1

a) Can you write 3 numbers with a median of 4 and a range of 4?

b) Can you write 5 numbers with a median of 6 and a range of 8?

c) Make up some more questions like this and ask a friend.

Exam tip

The mode is sometimes called the modal value.

EXAMPLE 1

These are the marks scored by Jean and David in six tests.

| Jean | 8 | 6 | 7 | 5 | 6 | 4 |
| David | 6 | 9 | 4 | 8 | 7 | 8 |

a) Work out the mean and range for Jean and David.

b) Compare the results.

a) Jean: Mean = $\frac{36}{6}$ = 6, Range = 8 − 4 = 4

David: Mean = $\frac{42}{6}$ = 7, Range = 9 − 4 = 5

b) David had a higher mean, so he scored better on average and was probably better at the subject. David's results were more spread out, showing he was less consistent.

EXAMPLE 2

The masses, in grams, of 12 potatoes in a bag bought from a supermarket were

    200   410   300   250   280   290   420   380   310   280   210   320

The masses, in grams, of 12 potatoes in a bag bought from a local greengrocer's shop were

    230   400   350   360   270   390   410   370   360   380   410   380

a) Work out the median and range for each bag of potatoes.

b) Compare the masses.

a) Supermarket masses in order

    200   210   250   280   280   290   300   310   320   380   410   420

The median is halfway between 290 and 300 so it is 295 g.

Range = 420 − 200 = 220 g.

Greengrocer's masses in order

    230   270   350   360   360   370   380   380   390   400   410   410

The median is halfway between 370 and 380 so it is 375 g.

Range = 410 − 230 = 190 g.

b) The potatoes from the greengrocer are heavier on average, and also more around the same weight, than the ones from the supermarket.

EXAMPLE 3

At the local shoe shop fifteen pairs of ladies' shoes were sold (they did not sell half sizes). The sizes were

    3, 5, 6, 3, 3, 4, 4, 5, 5, 5, 5, 7, 3, 4 and 4

a) Work out the mean, median and mode for these sizes.

b) Which measure of average is the most useful, and why?

a) Mean = 66 ÷ 15 = 4·9

Median: In order the sizes are 3, 3, 3, 3, 4, 4, 4, 4, 5, 5, 5, 5, 5, 6, 7

So the median is 4.   **The median is the middle one.**

The mode is 5.   **The mode is the most popular one.**

b) The most useful measure in this case is the mode, because it can be used to find out of which size to order most.

> ### Exam tip
> When you are asked to compare two sets of data, it is not enough just to say that one has a larger mean and a larger range. You need to comment about the size on average and the spread.

If you are asked which is the best measure of average it, depends on the circumstances.

Usually the mean is the best measure as every value is used to work it out.

The median is sometimes the best measure because one extreme value can affect the mean.

The mode is sometimes the best measure as you may need to know which is the most common value.

Exam tip

Some sets of data will not have a mode.

EXERCISE 5.1A

The first question is simply revision of working out the averages.

1 Find the mean, median, mode and range of these sets of data.

   a) 8, 10, 12, 7, 7, 6, 7, 7, 8

   b) 1, 3, 5, 7, 9, 4, 2, 5

   c) 47, 48, 41, 49, 45, 48, 48, 42, 43, 44

   d) 129, 125, 138, 147, 126, 134, 139

   e) 634, 635, 639, 621, 674, 671, 666, 632

2 The number of points scored by two shooters, Carl and Adam, in a basketball team in eight games are in the table.

Carl	17	19	21	24	16	18	14	23
Adam	19	20	14	25	26	29	12	13

   a) Work out the mean and range for each man.

   b) Compare their points scored.

3 Cars were checked for speed on a main road at 8 a.m. and at 10 a.m.

   These were the speeds in miles per hour of the first 10 cars recorded at both those times.

8 a.m.	40	45	43	47	42	48	51	47	46	45
10 a.m.	38	36	35	39	43	42	39	46	45	41

   a) Work out the mean, median and range of the speeds at the two times.

   b) Compare the speeds at the two times.

Exercise 5.1A cont'd

4 These are the scores, out of 50, won by Cathy and Mary in the last ten quizzes at the Bluebell pub.

Cathy	38	30	40	49	32	31	35	28	38	33
Mary	39	32	39	36	32	32	34	31	38	38

a) Work out the mean and range for each of the women.

b) Which would you pick for the team, and why?

5 At a gymnastics competition Margo was given the following marks by the ten judges.

8·7, 8·9, 9·3, 9·1, 8·4, 8·1, 8·9, 9·1, 9·2, 9·1

a) Work out the mean, the median and the range for Margo.

b) Janice had a mean of 9·1, a median of 8·8 and a range of 1·6. Which is the better average to use to compare the two girls? Give a reason for your answer.

EXERCISE 5.1B

The first question is simply revision of working out the average and range.

1 Find the mean, median, mode and range of these sets of data.

a) 10, 5, 12, 6, 9, 6, 8

b) 11, 12, 15, 15, 11, 12, 12, 16

c) 7, 8, 9, 9, 5, 8, 8, 4, 5

d) 419, 425, 421, 418, 417

e) 723, 713, 713, 722, 747, 737, 726, 751

2 The number of hours of sunshine in June during the last eight years at two holiday resorts, Cambeach and Sponsea, are given in the table.

Cambeach	180	170	109	171	165	190	162	173
Sponsea	170	168	120	172	158	178	157	169

a) Work out the mean, median and range for each resort.

b) Compare the amount of sunshine at the two resorts.

Exercise 5.1B cont'd

3 Twenty-four people decided to diet.

Twelve used the B diet and their weight losses, in pounds, over four weeks were

    8, 6, 4, 6, 4, 7, 4, 5, 9, 8, 7, 6.

Twelve used the T diet and their weight losses, in pounds, over a four week period were

    5, 12, 3, 4, 5, 6, 5, 4, 5, 5, 6, 6.

a) Work out the mean and range for each diet.

b) Compare the effectiveness of the diets.

4 The wages, per year, of the 12 workers at Tympon Engineering are

£54 000, £21 000, £24 000, £22 000, £24 000, £41 000, £25 000, £26 000, £24 000, £26 000, £28 000, £24 000

a) Work out the mean, median and range of the wages.

b) In a speech, the chairman claimed that the average wage was over £28 000. Comment on this statement.

5 Halif and Brian both play cricket for the school team. Their last eight scores are in the table.

Halif	23	24	21	24	24	23	26	23
Brian	33	19	16	0	32	34	16	30

a) Work out their mean and range.

b) Compare the batsmen.

Key ideas

● When comparing distributions, you need to consider the range as well as the measure of average.

● The best average to use for a specific question depends on the context.

6 Multiplying and dividing without calculators

You should already know

● how to multiply and divide simple numbers such as 9 × 7, 48 ÷ 6.

You must not use a calculator to answer any of the questions in this chapter.

Multiplication

ACTIVITY 1

You can write 9 as 1 + 8, 2 + 7, and many other additions, as 10 − 1, 12 − 3 and many other subtractions, or as 3 × 3, 1 × 9, or as 18 ÷ 2 and so on.

Write the following in many ways, using other numbers

a) 2,   **b)** 5,   **c)** 10,   **d)** 12

e) Choose some other numbers to write in other ways yourself.

As it says at the beginning of the chapter you should already be able to multiply simple numbers. Look now at these examples.

EXAMPLE 1

Work out **a)** 46 × 4   **b)** 57 × 6   **c)** 214 × 7

a) There are various ways to work these out.

Method 1

46 × 4 = 40 × 4 + 6 × 4

= 160 + 24 = 184

Example 1 cont'd

Method 2

```
    4 6
×     4
  18²4
```

6 × 4 = 24 (4 down and 2 to carry)

4 × 4 = 16 + 2 = 18

b)
```
    5 7
×     6
  34⁴2
```

7 × 6 = 42, 2 down and 4 to carry

5 × 6 = 30 + 4 = 34

Answer is 342.

c)
```
    2 8 4
×       7
  19⁵8²8
```

4 × 7 = 28, 8 down, 2 to carry

8 ¥ 7 = 56 + 2 = 58, 8 down and 5 to carry

2 × 7 = 14 + 5 = 19.

Answer is 1988.

Method 2 is the most useful, especially when harder questions are involved and this is only the first step.

EXAMPLE 2

Work out **a)** 14 × 40   **b)** 37 × 60

a) 14 × 40 = 14 × 4 × 10 = 56 × 10 = 560

b) 37 × 60 = 37 × 6 × 10 = 222 × 10 = 2220

Work out 14 × 4 as in Example 1 above and then multiply by 10.

EXERCISE 6.1A

Work out

1 a) 27 × 5	**b)** 36 × 6	**c)** 48 × 4	**d)** 19 × 8	**e)** 52 × 7
2 a) 49 × 8	**b)** 83 × 7	**c)** 62 × 9	**d)** 84 × 6	**e)** 67 × 7
3 a) 28 × 50	**b)** 46 × 60	**c)** 27 × 80	**d)** 93 × 30	**e)** 45 × 90
4 a) 138 × 3	**b)** 264 × 7	**c)** 581 × 9	**d)** 843 × 6	**e)** 218 × 5

EXERCISE 6.1B

Work out

	a)	b)	c)	d)	e)
1	**a)** 17×6	**b)** 46×5	**c)** 38×3	**d)** 15×8	**e)** 72×4
2	**a)** 29×8	**b)** 57×7	**c)** 65×9	**d)** 78×6	**e)** 75×7
3	**a)** 59×50	**b)** 63×60	**c)** 72×80	**d)** 87×40	**e)** 26×90
4	**a)** 218×6	**b)** 614×7	**c)** 271×9	**d)** 853×4	**e)** 918×5

You need to be able to calculate the answers to harder questions like

$$476 \times 46$$

without using a calculator.

Here are some methods that you may have seen before. Make sure you can follow the thinking involved in each one.

a)

```
        476
  ×      46
     19 040  ←(476 × 40)
      2 856  ←(476 × 6)
     21 896
```

b)

```
        476
  ×      46
     18 400  ←(400 × 46)
      3 220  ←(70 × 46)
        276  ←(6 × 46)
     21 896
```

c) Using a grid:

×	400	70	6		
40	16 000	2800	240	=	19 040
6	2 400	420	36	=	+ 2 856
					21 896

d) By doubling:

$$472 \times 1 = 476$$
$$476 \times 2 = 952$$
$$476 \times 4 = 1904$$
$$476 \times 8 = 3808$$
$$476 \times 16 = 7616$$
$$476 \times 32 = 15\,232$$

Now $46 = 32 + 8 + 4 + 2$

So $476 \times 46 = 476 \times 32 + 476 \times 8 + 476 \times 4 + 476 \times 2$
$$= 15\,232 + 3808 + 1904 + 952$$
$$= 21\,896$$

e) This method is sometimes called the lattice method.

Draw a lattice as shown.

Multiply along the lattice lines filling in the answers to each multiplication as shown, until

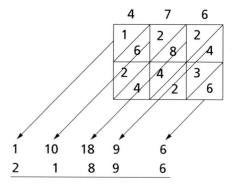

Add along the diagonal lines and carry the 'tens' digit to the next column as shown.

EXERCISE 6.2A

Choose one of the methods shown above or any other method that you feel happy using and work out the answers to the following questions.

1   **a)** 27×15 **b)** 36×16 **c)** 48×12 **d)** 19×21 **e)** 52×41

2   **a)** 49×18 **b)** 83×27 **c)** 62×39 **d)** 84×61 **e)** 67×72

3   **a)** 28×51 **b)** 46×64 **c)** 27×83 **d)** 93×32 **e)** 45×29

4   **a)** 138×13 **b)** 264×12 **c)** 581×23 **d)** 843×16 **e)** 218×15

5   **a)** 705×32 **b)** 46×79 **c)** 867×34

    d) 712×63 **e)** 976×46 **f)** 373×73

6   **a)** 624×75 **b)** 416×73 **c)** 973×92

    d) 504×56 **e)** 839×79 **f)** 415×235

7   A cinema has 54 seats along each row. The rows are labelled A, B, C, etc. up to Y. How many seats are there altogether?

8   A school has 25 classes. There are 29 pupils in each class. How many pupils are there altogether?

9   A railway wagon can carry 21 crates in a layer and there are eight layers on each wagon. How many crates will there be in a train 32 wagons long?

10 A painter buys 86 tins of paint at 98p each. How much does he spend?

EXERCISE 6.2B

Choose one of the methods shown above or any other method that you feel happy using and work out the answers to the following questions.

1   **a)** 17×11 **b)** 46×12 **c)** 38×13 **d)** 15×14 **e)** 72×15

2   **a)** 29×24 **b)** 57×23 **c)** 65×25 **d)** 78×16 **e)** 75×71

3   **a)** 59×52 **b)** 63×61 **c)** 72×82 **d)** 87×41 **e)** 26×93

4   **a)** 218×12 **b)** 614×14 **c)** 271×15 **d)** 853×16 **e)** 918×51

5   **a)** 615×46 **b)** 54×82 **c)** 932×42

    d) 422×65 **e)** 428×64 **f)** 737×37

6   **a)** 624×74 **b)** 641×37 **c)** 379×29

    d) 405×65 **e)** 938×97 **f)** 514×523

Chapter 6   *Multiplying and dividing without calculators*

Exercise 6.2B cont'd

7 A lecture theatre has 42 rows. There are 24 seats on each row. How many seats are there altogether?

8 A university course has the following number of students:

Year 1: 6 groups of 24 students   Year 2: 5 groups of 20 students

Year 3: 5 groups of 22 students   Year 4: 5 groups of 19 students.

How many students are there altogether?

9 16 wine bottles fit into a cardboard carrying case. How many wine bottles are there in a van load of 132 carrying cases?

10 Arthur buys 25 packets of soup at 59p each. How much does he pay?

Division

Before going on to harder division questions you need to check that you can divide simple numbers.

EXAMPLE 3

Work out

a) $48 \div 6$ **b)** $45 \div 5$ **c)** $147 \div 3$ **d)** $296 \div 8$

a) $48 \div 6 = 8$

This you should know by going through your 6 times table ($8 \times 6 = 48$).

b) $45 \div 5 = 9$

This you should know by going through your 5 times table ($9 \times 5 = 45$).

c) $3\lfloor 14^27$
Answer = 49

$14 \div 3 = 4$ rem 2; $27 \div 3 = 9$.

d) $8\lfloor 29^56$
Answer = 37

$29 \div 8 = 3$ rem 5; $56 \div 8 = 7$.

Exam tip

If you do not know how many times 8 goes into 29, say, write down your 8 times table until you pass 29. In this case you will get as far as $4 \times 8 = 32$, which is too big. So $3 \times 8 = 24$ is correct and there is a remainder of 5.

In division you need to be able to calculate the answers to questions without using a calculator.

$$816 \div 34 =$$
$$732 \div 14 =$$

The actual method you use isn't important but you should be able to explain how the method works.

Here are some methods you may have seen before.

a) $816 \div 34 = 245$ $732 \div 14 = 52$ rem 4

$$
\begin{array}{r}
24 \\
34\overline{)816} \\
-680 \quad [= 34 \times 20] \\
\hline
136 \\
-136 \quad [= 34 \times 4] \\
\hline
0
\end{array}
$$

$$
\begin{array}{r}
52 \\
14\overline{)732} \\
-700 \quad [= 14 \times 5] \\
\hline
32 \\
-28 \quad [= 14 \times 2] \\
\hline
4
\end{array}
$$

b) $816 \div 34$ $732 \div 14$

$$
\begin{array}{r}
816 \\
-340 \quad [= 34 \times 10] \\
\hline
476 \\
-340 \quad [= 34 \times 10] \\
\hline
136 \\
-136 \quad [= 34 \times 4] \\
\hline
0
\end{array}
$$

Answer is $10 + 10 + 4 = 24$

$$
\begin{array}{r}
732 \\
-140 \quad [= 14 \times 10] \\
\hline
592 \\
-140 \quad [= 14 \times 10] \\
\hline
452 \\
-140 \quad [= 14 \times 10] \\
\hline
312 \\
-140 \quad [= 14 \times 10] \\
\hline
172 \\
-140 \quad [= 14 \times 10] \\
\hline
32 \\
-28 \quad [= 14 \times 2] \\
\hline
4
\end{array}
$$

Answer is $10 + 10 + 10 + 10 + 10 + 2 =$ 52 remainder 4.

EXERCISE 6.3A

Work out questions 1–5 without using a calculator.

1 **a)** $48 \div 4$ **b)** $64 \div 2$ **c)** $72 \div 3$ **d)** $85 \div 5$ **e)** $96 \div 6$.

2 **a)** $91 \div 7$ **b)** $120 \div 8$ **c)** $144 \div 9$ **d)** $242 \div 11$ **e)** $168 \div 12$.

3 **a)** $252 \div 4$ **b)** $102 \div 6$ **c)** $315 \div 7$ **d)** $456 \div 8$ **e)** $333 \div 9$.

4 **a)** $1029 \div 21$ **b)** $684 \div 18$ **c)** $1344 \div 16$
    d) $2604 \div 28$ **e)** $2272 \div 32$ **f)** $352 \div 22$.

Chapter 6   *Multiplying and dividing without calculators*

Exercise 6.3A cont'd

5 **a)** $672 \div 21$ **b)** $425 \div 17$ **c)** $576 \div 32$
    d) $247 \div 19$ **e)** $875 \div 25$ **f)** $574 \div 26$.

6   Eggs are packed in boxes of 12. How many boxes will be needed for 828 eggs?

7   The school canteen sits six to a table. There are 148 pupils eating.
    How many tables do they need?

8   A box hold 16 tins. There are 352 tins. How many boxes do we need?

EXERCISE 6.3B

Work out questions 1–5 without using a calculator.

1 **a)** $84 \div 4$ **b)** $74 \div 2$ **c)** $84 \div 3$ **d)** $105 \div 5$ **e)** $102 \div 6$.

2 **a)** $84 \div 7$ **b)** $112 \div 8$ **c)** $153 \div 9$ **d)** $143 \div 13$ **e)** $294 \div 14$.

3 **a)** $252 \div 6$ **b)** $108 \div 4$ **c)** $665 \div 7$ **d)** $504 \div 8$ **e)** $468 \div 9$.

4 **a)** $1665 \div 45$ **b)** $576 \div 18$ **c)** $1120 \div 32$
    d) $2184 \div 84$ **e)** $2176 \div 32$ **f)** $418 \div 22$.

5 **a)** $312 \div 13$ **b)** $882 \div 63$ **c)** $704 \div 32$
    d) $342 \div 19$ **e)** $975 \div 25$ **f)** $560 \div 26$.

6   640 children and teachers from a school are going on a coach. Each coach can carry 54 people. How many coaches are needed?

7   Chairs in the school hall are arranged in rows of 22. If the caretaker needs to seat 396 for a concert, how many rows should he set out?

8   A car transporter holds 12 cars. We need to transport 185 cars. How many trips are needed?

Key ideas

- When multiplying or dividing without a calculator, show all the steps of your working.
- If in doubt of any times table, write down the full table and pick out the one you need.

7 *Formulae*

You should already know

- how to multiply simple numbers
- how to work out n^2 and n^3 where n is a whole number or decimal
- how to multiply a simple fraction by a whole number.
- that ab means $a \times b$ and $2a$ means $2 \times a$
- that $x + x = 2x$; $x + 2 + x + 3 = 2x + 5$ etc.

ACTIVITY 1

Write these out as fully as possible, e.g. $2a^2 = 2 \times a \times a$.

(i) ab **(ii)** a^2 **(iii)** $5a$ **(iv)** $3ab$ **(v)** a^2b **(vi)** c^3

(vii) $2b^2$ **(viii)** abc **(ix)** $2at^2$ **(x)** $4a^2bc^3$

Write these as simply as possible.

(i) $a + 2a$ **(ii)** $3y + y$ **(iii)** $13x + x + 3$ **(iv)** $2c + 4 + 3c + 1$ **(v)** $d + 3 + d + 3 + d + 2d$

Substitution in formulae

The easiest formulae are those with just one term that only involves multiplication, or with two terms but only involving addition or subtraction.

EXAMPLE 1

For the formula $P = 2ab$, find P when

a) $a = 3$, $b = 5$ **b)** $a = 6$, $b = \frac{1}{2}$ **c)** $a = 3.2$, $b = 2.5$

a) $P = 2 \times 3 \times 5 = 30$

b) $P = 2 \times 6 \times \frac{1}{2} = 12 \times \frac{1}{2} = 6$

c) $P = 2 \times 3.2 \times 2.5 = 16$

A calculator may be used in **c)**.

EXAMPLE 2

For the formula $A = a + b - c$, find A when
a) $a = 3$, $b = 5$, $c = 6$ **b)** $a = 13.2$, $b = 12.5$, $c = 14.6$
a) $A = 3 + 5 - 6 = 2$
b) $A = 13.2 + 12.5 - 14.6 = 11.1$

Exam tip

$3a^2$ means $3 \times a \times a$. A common error is to work out $3a$ and then square the result.

EXAMPLE 3

For the formula $B = 2a^3$, find B when
a) $a = 6$,   **b)** $a = 3.6$
a) $B = 2 \times 6 \times 6 \times 6 = 432$

a^3 means $a \times a \times a$.

b) $B = 2 \times 3.6 \times 3.6 \times 3.6 = 93.312$ **Both parts may need a calculator.**

EXERCISE 7.1A

1 For the formula $C = 2a$ find C when
   a) $a = 3$ **b)** $a = 3.2$ **c)** $a = \frac{1}{2}$
2 For the formula $D = a - b$, find D when
   a) $a = 8$, $b = 5$ **b)** $a = 73$, $b = 15$ **c)** $a = 8.5$, $b = 2.3$
3 For the formula $E = 5ab$, find E when
   a) $a = 3$, $b = 2$ **b)** $a = 6$, $b = \frac{1}{2}$ **c)** $a = 20$, $b = 4$
4 For the formula $F = abc$, find F when
   a) $a = 1$, $b = 3$, $c = 2$ **b)** $a = 6$, $b = \frac{1}{4}$, $c = 2$ **c)** $a = 4$, $b = 2$, $c = 1.5$
5 For the formula $G = a - b + c$, find G when
   a) $a = 8$, $b = 5$, $c = 6$ **b)** $a = 2$, $b = 4$, $c = 7$ **c)** $a = 13.2$, $b = 12.5$, $c = 14.6$
6 For the formula $H = 3a^2$, find H when
   a) $a = 2$ **b)** $a = 5$ **c)** $a = 8$
7 For the formula $I = a^2b$, find I when
   a) $a = 2$, $b = 1$ **b)** $a = 3$, $b = 5$ **c)** $a = 6$, $b = 2$
8 For the formula $J = 5b^3$, find J when
   a) $b = 2$ **b)** $b = 3$ **c)** $b = 1$

Exercise 7.1A cont'd

9 The formula for cooking a piece of meat is given by $T = 40w + 20$ where w is the mass in kilograms and T is the cooking time in minutes. Find the time to cook a piece of meat of mass

a) 2 kg **b)** 4 kg **c)** 3·5 kg.

10 The area of a rectangle is $A = ab$ where a and b are the length and width of the rectangle.

Find the area if

a) $a = 3$ cm, $b = 4$ cm **b)** $a = 35$ mm, $b = 40$ mm.

EXERCISE 7.1B

You may use a calculator in this exercise.

1 For the formula $C = 4a$ find, C when

a) $a = 6$ **b)** $a = 3·6$ **c)** $a = 5·84$.

2 For the formula $D = a - b$, find D when

a) $a = 9$, $b = 3$ **b)** $a = 8·75$, $b = 5·32$ **c)** $a = 73·8$, $b = 15·95$.

3 For the formula $E = 8ab$, find E when

a) $a = 3$, $b = 2$ **b)** $a = 2$, $b = \frac{1}{4}$ **c)** $a = 2·5$, $b = 4·6$.

4 For the formula $F = abc$, find F when

a) $a = 11$, $b = 3$, $c = 6$ **b)** $a = 8$, $b = \frac{1}{4}$, $c = \frac{1}{2}$ **c)** $a = 4·2$, $b = 2·1$, $c = 1·5$.

5 For the formula $G = a + b - c$, find G when

a) $a = 4$, $b = 5$, $c = 3$ **b)** $a = 2$, $b = 4$, $c = 6$ **c)** $a = 1·32$, $b = 2·5$, $c = 1·46$.

6 For the formula $H = 8a^2$ find H when

a) $a = 2$ **b)** $a = 1·5$ **c)** $a = 2·8$.

7 For the formula $I = a^2b$, find I when

a) $a = 2$, $b = 1·5$ **b)** $a = 3·6$, $b = 5$ **c)** $a = 6·4$, $b = 2·8$.

8 For the formula $J = b^3$, find J when

a) $a = 2·6$ **b)** $b = 3·9$ **c)** $b = 12·5$.

9 The approximate perimeter of a circle (called the circumference) is given by $C = 3r$ where C is the circumference and r is the radius of the circle. Calculate the circumference of a circle whose radius is **a)** 5 cm **b)** 12 cm **c)** 25 mm.

10 The area of a trapezium is given by $A = \frac{1}{2}ah + \frac{1}{2}bh$

Use this formula to find A when $a = 6$ mm, $b = 8$ mm and $h = 4$ mm.

EXAMPLE 4

For the formula $F = 7 + 2a$, work out F when

a) $a = 3$, **b)** $a = \frac{1}{2}$ **c)** $a = 3.7$

a) $F = 7 + 2 \times 3 = 7 + 6 = 13$

$2a$ means $2 \times a$

b) $F = 7 + 2 \times \frac{1}{2} = 7 + 1 = 8$

c) $F = 7 + 2 \times 3.7 = 7 + 7.4 = 14.4$

This can be done either with or without a calculator.

Exam tip

When working out a formula with two steps, work out each part separately first.

EXAMPLE 5

For the formula $G = a^2 + 2b$, work out G when

a) $a = 3$, $b = 2$ **b)** $a = 6$, $b = \frac{1}{2}$ **c)** $a = 3.7$, $b = 5.2$

a) $G = 3 \times 3 + 2 \times 2 = 9 + 4 = 13$

b) $G = 6 \times 6 + 2 \times \frac{1}{2} = 36 + 1 = 37$

c) $G = 3.7 \times 3.7 + 2 \times 5.2 = 13.69 + 10.4 = 24.09$

EXAMPLE 6

$T = \dfrac{3a + 2b}{10}$

Work out T when **a)** $a = 6$, $b = 11$ **b)** $a = 4.3$, $b = 1.55$

a) $T = \dfrac{3 \times 6 + 2 \times 11}{10} = \dfrac{18 + 22}{10} = \dfrac{40}{10} = 4$

b) $T = \dfrac{3 \times 4.3 + 2 \times 1.55}{10} = \dfrac{12.9 + 3.1}{10} = \dfrac{16}{10} = 1.6$

EXAMPLE 7

The formula for the volume of a cuboid is

$A = a \times b \times c$

when the sides are a, b and c in length.

Find A when

a) $a = 2$, $b = 4$, $c = 6$

b) $a = 5.5$, $b = 2.8$, $c = 3.7$

a) $A = 2 \times 4 \times 6 = 48$

b) $A = 5.5 \times 2.8 \times 3.7 = 56.98$

EXERCISE 7.2A

1 $B = 15 + 4t$. Find B when   **a)** $t = 3$ **b)** $t = 2{\cdot}5$ **c)** $t = \frac{1}{4}$.

2 $C = 20 - 2u$. Find C when   **a)** $u = 2$ **b)** $u = 3{\cdot}5$ **c)** $u = \frac{1}{4}$.

3 $D = 5v - 1$. Find D when   **a)** $v = 6$ **b)** $v = 3{\cdot}2$ **c)** $v = \frac{1}{2}$.

4 $E = 6c + 2d$. Find E when   **a)** $c = 2, d = 5$ **b)** $c = 3, d = \frac{1}{2}$

          c) $c = 2{\cdot}5, d = 1{\cdot}5$.

5 $F = 3e - f$. Find F when   **a)** $e = 9, f = 7$ **b)** $e = 6, f = 2{\cdot}4$ **c)** $e = 1, f = \frac{1}{2}$.

6 $G = p^2 + 2pq$. Find G when   **a)** $p = 4, q = 2$ **b)** $p = 5, q = 2{\cdot}4$ **c)** $p = 4, q = \frac{1}{4}$.

7 $H = r^3 + rs$. Find H when   **a)** $r = 2, s = 6$ **b)** $r = 3, s = 5$ **c)** $r = 4, s = \frac{1}{2}$.

8 The area of a rectangle is given by the formula $A = l \times b$, when l is the length and b the width. Work out the area when

   a) $l = 4, b = 3$ **b)** $l = 5{\cdot}4, b = 5$ **c)** $l = 12\frac{1}{2}, b = 4$.

9 The cost in pounds of an advert in the *Mercury* magazine is given by the formula

   $C = 2 + \frac{w}{5}$, where w is the number of words in the advert. Find C when

   a) $w = 25$ **b)** $w = 48$

10

The AC bus company estimates the time for a bus journey in minutes by using the formula

$T = 12m + 2s$, where m is the length of the journey in miles and s is the number of bus stops.

   a) Find T when **(i)** $m = 5, s = 35$ **(ii)** $m = 3{\cdot}5, s = 24$

   b) How long does the company estimate is the time of a journey of 8 miles with 20 bus stops?

EXERCISE 7.2B

You may use a calculator in this exercise.

1 $A = 10 + a$. Find A when **a)** $a = 2\cdot5$ **b)** $a = 5\cdot7$ **c)** $a = \frac{1}{2}$.

2 $B = 12\cdot5 - 3b$. Find B when **a)** $b = 2\cdot6$ **b)** $b = 1\cdot7$ **c)** $b = 0$.

3 $C = e^2 - 1$. Find C when **a)** $e = 2\cdot4$ **b)** $e = 1\cdot2$ **c)** $e = 3\frac{1}{2}$.

4 $D = 4a + 3b$. Find D when **a)** $a = 1$, $b = 0$ **b)** $a = 6\cdot3$, $b = 2\cdot5$ **c)** $a = 2\cdot4$, $b = 3\cdot6$.

5 $E = p^2 + q^2$. Find E when **a)** $p = 9$, $q = 3$ **b)** $p = 6\cdot8$, $q = 2\cdot5$ **c)** $p = 3$, $q = \frac{1}{2}$.

6 $F = ab^2$. Find G when **a)** $a = 4$, $b = 2$ **b)** $a = 2\cdot6$, $b = 2\cdot4$ **c)** $a = 56$, $b = \frac{1}{2}$.

7 $G = 2r^2 + s$. Find G when **a)** $r = 3$, $s = 6$ **b)** $r = 3\cdot4$, $s = 5\cdot2$ **c)** $r = 1\cdot3$, $s = 2$.

8

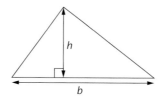

The area of a triangle is given by the formula $A = b \times h \div 2$, when b is the base and h the vertical height.

Work out the area when **a)** $b = 3\cdot5$, $h = 6$ **b)** $b = 5\cdot2$, $h = 3$ **c)** $b = 4$, $h = 1\cdot6$.

9 The formula for the time in hours taken for a journey is

$t = \frac{d}{s}$ where d is the distance in kilometres and s is the speed in kilometres per hour.

Find t when **a)** $d = 157\cdot5$, $s = 45$ **b)** $d = 300$, $s = 37\cdot5$.

10 A formula to find the distance travelled by a body is

$v = u + at$

Use this formula to find the speed v when

a) $u = 3$, $t = 5$, $a = 3$ **b)** $u = 3\cdot6$, $t = 4\cdot5$, $a = 4.2$.

Deriving a simple formula

Imagine you had a job where you were paid by the hour. You would receive the same amount for each hour you worked.

How could you work out how much you would earn in a week?

You would need to work it out as:

> the number of hours worked multiplied by the amount you are paid for each hour.

This is a **formula** in words.

If you work 35 hours at £4.50 an hour, it is easy to work out 35 × £4.50, but what if the numbers change? The calculation '35 × £4.50' is only right if you work 35 hours. Suppose you move to a better job where you are paid more for each hour?

You need a simple formula that always works. You can use symbols to stand for the numbers that can change. You could use ? or □ , but it is less confusing to use letters.

Start by using algebra to work out your wages.

Let: the number of hours be N

the amount you are paid each hour be P

the amount you earn in a week be W.

Then $W = N \times P = NP$

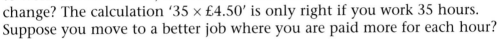

EXAMPLE 7

Find W when $N = 40$, $P = £5.00$.

$W = 40 \times 5 = £200$

EXAMPLE 8

When you make a journey, S is the speed, d is the distance travelled and t is the time taken.

To find the speed, you divide the distance by the time, so the formula for S is:

$S = \frac{d}{t}$

EXAMPLE 9

The width of a rectangle is x cm and the length is 5 cm longer.

Find the formula for the perimeter, P, of the rectangle in terms of x.

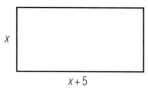

The length is $x + 5$

so the perimeter $P = x + x + 5 + x + x + 5$

$P = 4x + 10$.

> **Exam tip**
>
> It is helpful to work out any intermediate parts first when you are finding a formula. In Example 9, the length was worked out first.

> **Exam tip**
>
> If you are not sure whether to multiply or divide, try an example with numbers first

EXAMPLE 10

The cost (C) of hiring a car is a fixed charge (f), plus the number of days (n) multiplied by the daily rate (d), so:

$c = f + n \times d = f + nd$

EXERCISE 7.3A

Write these formulae using the letters given.

1 The area (A) of a rectangle which is equal to the length (l) multiplied by the width (w).

2 The cost (C) of p kg of potatoes at d pence a kilogram.

3 The year of birth (Y) of a person x years old in the year 2000.

4 The distance (D), in miles, travelled in a car at s miles an hour in t hours.

5 The weight (W) of a shopping bag containing a kg of potatoes and c kg of carrots.

6 The time (T) to type a letter which is the number of words (w) divided by the number of words (r) typed in a minute.

7 The time (T) to cook a piece of beef weighing w kg if it takes s minutes per kilogram.

8 Joe's earnings (E) when he works h hours and is paid £x an hour.

9 The perimeter (P) of a rectangle with width (w) and length twice the width.

10 The cost (C) of hiring a tennis court for h hours when there is a fixed charge of £F and also a rate of £T an hour.

11 The volume (V) of a pyramid, which is the area (A) of the base, multiplied by the perpendicular height (h) divided by 3.

12 The perimeter (P) of a triangle with sides b, $b + 5$ and $2b$.

EXERCISE 7.3B

Write these formulae using the letters given.

1 The cost (C) of x concert tickets at £y each.

2 The area (A) of a parallelogram, which is the base (b) multiplied by the vertical height (h).

3 The cost in French francs (F) of a cardigan, which is the cost in pounds (L) multiplied by the exchange rate (e)

4 The height (H) cm, a person can touch on a wall, which is the person's height (t) cm, plus the height they can jump (j cm).

5 The sale price (S) of a coat, which is the normal price (N) minus the reduction (R).

6 The cost (C) of hiring a coach to go m miles, which is a fixed charge (F) plus £x a mile.

7 The average number of words (W) a child knows, which is its age in months (m) multiplied by 60 minus 900.

8 The number of tables (T) needed in a school canteen, which is the number of children (c) divided by the number at a table (b).

9 The perimeter (P) of a quadrilateral with sides x + 7, x + 5 and 2x − 1.

10 The total number of sweets (T) when Jason has x sweets, Basil has three more than Jason and David has twice as many as Basil.

11 The area (A) of a rectangle with width w and length twice the width.

12 The time (T) spent on a journey, which is the distance (D) travelled in the car divided by the speed (S) plus the time spent resting in the service station (R).

EXERCISE 7.4A

Use the formulae in Exercise 7.3A to find the following

1 A when l = 4 cm and w = 6 cm.
2 C when p = 8 and d = 12.
3 Y when x = 17.
4 D when s = 65 and t = 3.
5 W when a = 2·5 and c = 1·5.
6 T when w = 240 and r = 40.
7 T when w = 3·5 and s = 30.
8 E when h = 40 and x = 6.
9 P when w = 7.
10 C when h = 3, F = 10 and t = 4.
11 V when A = 24 and h = 5.
12 P when b = 6.

EXERCISE 7.4B

Use the formulae in Exercise 7.3A to find the following.

1 C when $x = 6$ and $y = 8{\cdot}75$.

2 A when $b = 3{\cdot}4$ and $h = 5{\cdot}3$.

3 F when $l = 39$ and $e = 10{\cdot}2$.

4 H when $t = 1{\cdot}35$ and $j = 0{\cdot}46$.

5 S when $n = 29{\cdot}99$, $r = 5{\cdot}50$.

6 C when $m = 220$, $f = 35$ and $x = 1{\cdot}40$.

7 W when $m = 24$.

8 T when $c = 102$ and $b = 6$.

9 P when $x = 4{\cdot}7$

10 T when $x = 9$.

11 A when $w = 3{\cdot}6$

12 T when $d = 225$, $s = 50$, $r = 2$.

Key ideas

● $2a^2$ means $2 \times a \times a$, not $2 \times a \times 2 \times a$.

● When substituting in a formula work out each term separately and then combine.

● When you have derived a formula you can always use numbers for the letters to check it if you are not sure.

8 Angle properties

You should already know

- how to use a protractor to measure an angle
- how to draw a straight line
- what acute, obtuse, reflex and right angles are.

ACTIVITY 1

Use your protractor to measure these angles.

a)   b)   c)   d)   e)

ACTIVITY 2

Use your protractor to draw angles of
a) 70°   **b)** 25°   **c)** 42°   **d)** 110°   **e)** 96°.

ACTIVITY 3

Look around your classroom and make a list of angles that are
a) acute   **b)** obtuse   **c)** right angles.

ACTIVITY 4

a) Here is a straight line with a point P marked on it.

Use your protractor to measure the angle marked.

b) Draw a straight line and on it mark a point. At the point draw another line outwards, making two angles on the line. Measure both angles. What should these two angles add up to?

c) Draw two lines crossing, forming four angles at the centre. Measure the four angles. What do you notice? Draw more crossing lines until you spot a rule.

d) Draw a point in the centre of your page and draw three or four lines coming from the point outwards. Measure all the angles at the centre. What should they add up to?

You should have found three angle facts.

1 **The sum of the angles on a straight line is 180°.**

2 **When two lines cross the opposite angles are equal.**

3 **The sum of the angles about a point is 360°.**

Angles that are opposite when two lines cross are called **vertically opposite**. The second rule is sometimes written as

Vertically opposite angles are equal.

EXAMPLE 1

Work out angles a, b and c. State a reason for your answer.

a)

b)

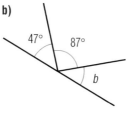

c)

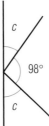

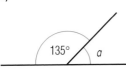

a) $135° + a = 180$ **The sum of angles on a straight line is 180°.**
$a = 45°$.

b) $47° + 87° + b = 180°$ **The sum of angles on a straight line is 180°**
$134° + b = 180°$
$b = 46°$.

c) $c + 98° + c = 180°$ **The sum of angles on a straight line is 180°**
$2c = 82°$
$c = 41°$.

Exam tip

The diagrams are not drawn to scale, so do not try to measure the answers.

Exam tip

In some questions you will be asked to give a reason for the answer. If you are asked to give a reason, state the angle fact you have used.

EXAMPLE 2

Work out the angles a, b, c, d and e. State a reason for your answer.

a)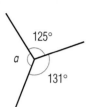

b)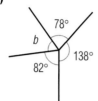

c)

a) $a + 125° + 131° = 360°$ The sum of the angles about a point is 360°.

$a + 256° = 360°$

$a = 104°$

b) $b + 78° + 138° + 82° = 360°$ The sum of the angles about a point is 360°.

$b + 298° = 360°$

$b = 62°$.

c) $c + 57° = 180$ The sum of the angles on a straight line is 180°.

$c = 113°$

$d = 57°$ Vertically opposite angles are equal.

$e = 113°$ Vertically opposite angles are equal.

Exam tip

Take care with your subtraction – it is useful to check by adding at the end. For example, in Example 2 a) check that 104°, 125° and 131° do add up to 360°.

EXERCISE 8.1A

1 Find the sizes of these lettered angles.

a)

b)

c)

d)

e)

f)

g)

h)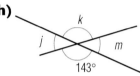

2 Two straight lines cross, making an angle of 35° between them. What are the sizes of the other three angles?

3 Two angles make up a straight line. One of them is 73°. What is the size of the other one?

4 Three angles make up a full turn round a point. They are all the same size. What size is each one?

5 Look at these angles and then copy the table below and complete it.

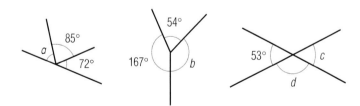

Angle	Size	Reason
a		The sum of angles on a straight line is ....
b		The sum of angles at a point is ....
c		........................angles are equal
d		The sum of angles ....

Exercise 8.1A cont'd

6 Find the angles *a*, *b* and *c*. Give reasons for your answers.

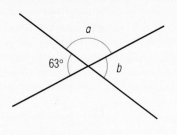

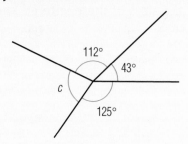

EXERCISE 8.1B

1 Find the sizes of these lettered angles.

a)

b)

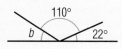

c)

d)

e)

f)

g)

h)

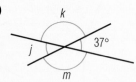

2 Two angles make up a straight line. One of them is 64°. What is the size of the other one?

3 Two lines cross and the obtuse angle between them is 121°. What is the acute angle between them?

4 Three angles make up a full turn round a point. Two are 125° and 146°. What is the size of the third angle?

Exercise 8.1B cont'd

5 Find the size of the angles marked with letters. Give reasons for your answers.

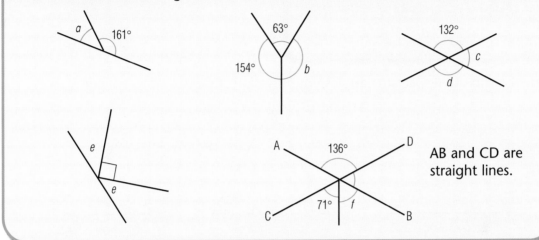

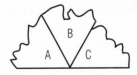

AB and CD are straight lines.

Triangles

Draw three triangles and measure the inside angles. What should they add up to?

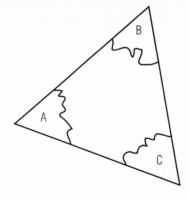

In the diagram above you can see that the three corners of the triangle have been torn off and put together to make a straight line. This gives a further angle fact.

The angles in a triangle add up to 180°.

ACTIVITY 6

Draw a triangle of your own, cut it out and tear off the corners.
Line them up to make a straight line.

Here are the three special triangles you have already met.

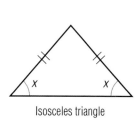

Isosceles triangle

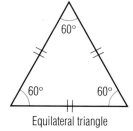

Equilateral triangle

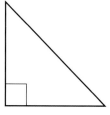

Right-angled triangle

An **isosceles triangle** has two angles the same and two sides the same.
An **equilateral triangle** has all three angles the same (60°) and all three sides the same.
A **right-angled triangle** has one angle of 90°.
A triangle that has all its angles different is called a **scalene triangle**.

These facts can be used to find angles.

ACTIVITY 7

Draw these triangles, and in each case state what type the triangle is.
a) With sides 3 cm, 4 cm and 5 cm
b) With sides 4 cm, 4 cm and 5 cm
c) With sides 5 cm, 5 cm and 5 cm
d) With sides 5 cm, 4 cm and 6 cm
e) With sides 5 cm, 5 cm and 3 cm.

EXAMPLE 3

Two angles of a triangle are 35 ° and 85 °. Work out the size of the third angle.

Third angle = 180 °− (35 ° + 85 °) = 180 °−120 ° = 60°.

EXAMPLE 4

In a isosceles triangle, work out the sizes of angles a and b. Give a reason for your answer.

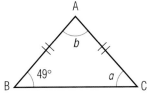

AB and AC are marked equal so the angles at B and C are the ones that are the same.

$a = 49°$

$b + 49°+ 49° = 180$

$b = 180° − 98° = 82°$.

Equal angles in an isosceles triangle.

Angles in a triangle add up to 180°.

EXAMPLE 5

In the right-angled triangle one of the other angles is 59 °. What is the size of the third angle?

Third angle is 90 ° − 59 ° = 31 °.

In a right-angled triangle the sum of the other two angles is 90 °.

EXAMPLE 6

Work out the sizes of the angles in the diagrams below. Sides the same length are marked with two short lines. Give reasons for your answers.

a)

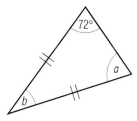

b)

c)

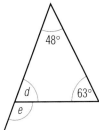

Example 6 cont'd

a) $a = 72°$

$b + 72° + 72° = 180°$ — Equal angles in an isosceles triangle.

$b + 144° = 180°$ — Angles in a triangle add up to 180°.

$b = 36°$.

b) $c + 63° = 90°$ — Other angles in a right-angled triangle add up to 90° *or* angles in a triangle add up to 180º.

$c = 27°$.

c) $d + 48° + 63° = 180°$

$d + 111° = 180°$ — Angles in a triangle add up to 180°.

$d = 79°$.

$e + 79° = 180°$ — The sum of angles on a straight line is 180°.

$e = 101°$.

EXERCISE 8.2A

1 A triangle has two angles, $114°$ and $27°$. Work out the size of the third angle.

2 A triangle has two angles, $74°$ and $32°$. Work out the size of the third angle. What is the special name of this triangle?

3 In an isosceles triangle the two angles that are the same are both $37°$. Work out the size of the third angle.

4 A right-angled triangle has an angle of $58°$. What is the size of the third angle?

5 A right-angled triangle is also isosceles. What is the size of each of the other two angles?

6 What can you say about the angles of an equilateral triangle?

7 Explain why a triangle cannot have two obtuse angles.

Exercise 8.2A cont'd

8 Work out the sizes of the angles in the diagrams below. Sides the same length are marked with two short lines. Give reasons for your answers.

a)

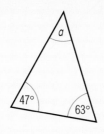

b)

c)

d)

e)

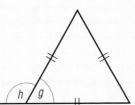

f)

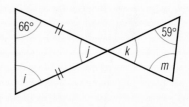

EXERCISE 8.2B

1 A triangle has two angles that are 12° and 67°. What size is of the third angle?

2 A triangle has two angles that are 89° and 41°. Work out the size of the third angle. What do you call this type of triangle?

3 In an isosceles triangle, one angle is 130°. The other two angles are the same as each other. Work out the size of one of these angles.

4 A right-angled triangle has an angle of 38°. What is the size of the third angle?

5 A triangle has two angles that are 63° and 27°. Work out the size of the third angle. What do you call this type of triangle?

6 One angle of an isosceles triangle is 92°. What sizes are the other two angles?

7 Draw an equilateral triangle as accurately as possible.

Exercise 8.2B cont'd

8 Work out the size of the angles in these diagrams. Sides the same length are marked with two short lines. Give reasons for your answers.

a)

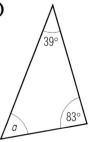

b)

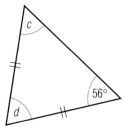

c)

d)

e)

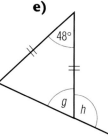

f)

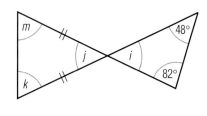

ACTIVITY 8

Draw two parallel lines and then draw one line crossing both these lines at an angle. Measure the angles you have made and see if you can find any rules for them.

Key ideas

- The sum of the angles on a straight line is 180°.
- The sum of the angles about a point is 360°.
- Vertically opposite angles are equal.
- The angles in a triangle add up to 180°.
- An isosceles triangle has two angles equal.
- An equilateral triangle has each angle equal to 60°.

B1 Revision exercise

1 These are the ages of the 12 members of the 'First Things First' youth group

12, 14, 14, 14, 15, 15, 16, 16, 17, 17, 18, 20

a) Find

    (i) the median

    (ii) the mode.

b) Which is the better average to represent the group?

2 These are the marks scored by Pauline and Phoebe in six tests

Pauline	8	7	8	4	9	6
Phoebe	6	7	5	6	4	8

a) Work out the mean and the range for each of the girls.

b) Who scored better on average in the tests?

c) Who was more consistent?

3 Do not use a calculator in this question.

Work out

a) 16×3 **b)** $90 \div 5$

c) 432×9 **d)** $624 \div 4$

e) 213×26 **f)** $384 \div 16$

g) 142×78 **h)** $840 \div 24$

i) 326×65 **j)** $918 \div 51$.

4 An office block has 24 windows on each of the six floors. A window cleaner charges 84p for each window. How much is he paid for the full building?

5 For the formula $S = 8a - 2b^2$, find S when

a) $a = 8$, $b = 3$ **b)** $a = 4.6$, $b = 2.5$

6 The cost C of renting a car is £b per day.

a) Write down a formula for the cost of hiring the car for d days.

b) Work out C when $b = 36$ and $d = 9$.

7 A rectangle is a cm wide. Its length, L, is 4 cm more than its width.

a) Write down an expression for L, in terms of a.

b) Write down a formula for the perimeter, P, in terms of a.

c) Work out the perimeter when $a = 5$.

8 Work out the angles marked a, b, c and d. Give reasons for each answer.

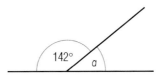

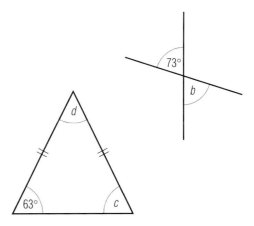

9 Reading from graphs

You should already know

- how to read points from a graph in all four quadrants
- how to read axes with scales marked in 1, 2 or 5 units.

ACTIVITY 1

a) On the scale below, what are the points marked A, B and C?

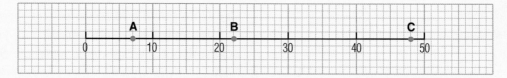

b) On the scale below, what are the points marked D, E and F?

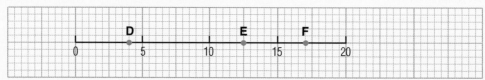

c) On the scale below, what are the points marked G, H, I and J?

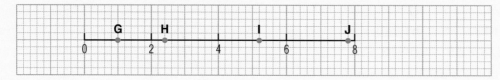

Activity 1 cont'd

d) On the scale below, what are the points marked K, L, M and N?

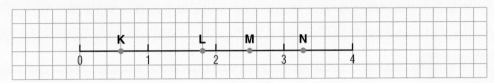

e) On the scale below, what are the points marked P, Q and R?

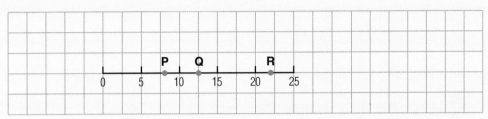

Algebraic graphs

You already know that the x-axis is horizontal and the y-axis is vertical.

If a straight line or a curve is drawn on a graph you need to be able to read from it.

EXAMPLE 1

The line drawn on the graph is $y = 3x - 5$.

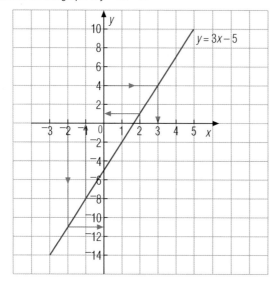

a) For the line $y = 3x - 5$, find the value of y when **(i)** $x = 2$ **(ii)** $x = {}^-2$.

b) For the line $y = 3x - 5$, find the value of x when **(i)** $y = 4$ **(ii)** $y = {}^-8$.

a) (i) $y = 1$ **(ii)** $y = {}^-11$

> Draw a line vertically from the x value on the x-axis until it meets the line and then horizontally from the line to the y-axis.

b) (i) $x = 3$ **(ii)** $x = {}^-1$.

> Draw a line horizontally from the y value on the y-axis until it meets the line and then vertically from the line to the x-axis.

EXAMPLE 2

On the grid below two graphs are drawn, $y = x^2 - 3x - 1$, and $y = 1 - 2x$.

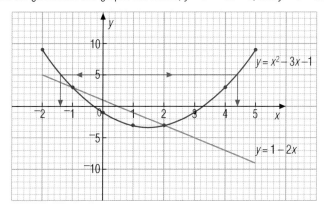

a) For the curve $y = x^2 - 3x - 1$, find the values of x when $y = 5$.

b) Find the coordinates where $y = 1 - 2x$ and $y = x^2 - 3x - 1$ cross.

a) $x = {}^-1{\cdot}4$ and $4{\cdot}4$

> **Draw a line horizontally from the y value on the y-axis until it meets the curve and then vertically from the curve to the x-axis.**

b) $({}^-1, 3)$ and $(2, {}^-3)$

> **Read the coordinates where the line and the curve cross.**

Exam tip

Be careful when reading scales – always check what each small square represents. It is helpful to use a ruler and a setsquare to read from graphs.

EXERCISE 9.1A

1 The line drawn on the graph is $y = 2x + 3$.

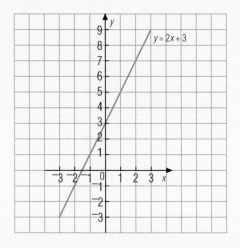

For the line,

    a) find the value of y when **(i)** $x = 2$ **(ii)** $x = {}^-1$

    b) find the value of x when **(i)** $y = 5$ **(ii)** $y = {}^-2$.

2 The line drawn on the graph is $y = 1 - 2x$.

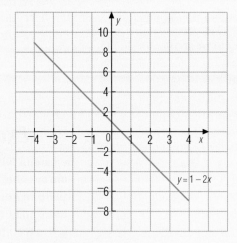

For the line,

    a) find the value of y when **(i)** $x = 2$ **(ii)** $x = {}^-3$

    b) find the value of x when **(i)** $y = 3$ **(ii)** $y = {}^-5$.

Exercise 9.1A cont'd

3 The curve drawn on the graph is $y = x^2 + 3x$.

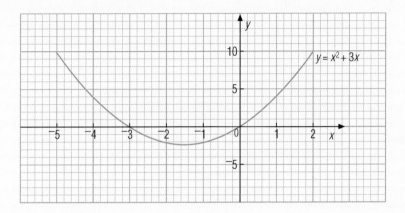

For the curve,
a) find the value of y when **(i)** $x = 2$ **(ii)** $x = {}^-1$
b) find the value of x when $y = 5$.

4 The curve drawn on the graph is $y = x^2 - 2x - 3$.

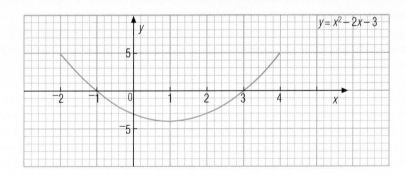

For the curve,
a) find the value of y when **(i)** x = 2 **(ii)** $x = {}^-2$.
b) find the value of x when $y = {}^-2$.

Exercise 9.1A cont'd

5 Two graphs are drawn on the grid, $y = 4x^2 - 5$ and $y = 3x + 2$.

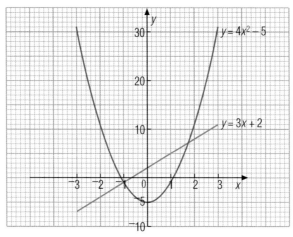

a) For the curve $y = 4x^2 - 5$, find the values of x when $y = 20$.

b) Find the coordinates where $y = 3x + 2$ and $y = 4x^2 - 5$ cross.

EXERCISE 9.1B

1 The line drawn on the graph is $y = 3x - 4$.

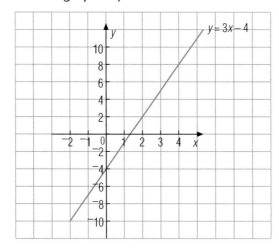

For the line,

    a) find the value of y when **(i)** $x = 2$ **(ii)** $x = 0$

    b) find the value of x when **(i)** $y = 5$ **(ii)** $y = ^-7$.

Exercise 9.1B cont'd

2 The line drawn on the graph is $y = 5 - 2x$.

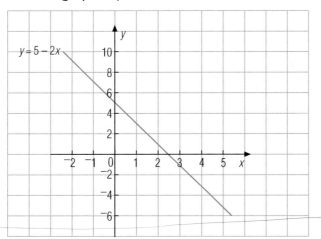

For the line,
    a) find the value of y when **(i)** $x = 2$ **(ii)** $x = {}^-1$
    b) find the value of x when **(i)** $y = 5$ **(ii)** $y = {}^-3$.

3 The curve drawn on the graph is $y = x^2 - 3x$.

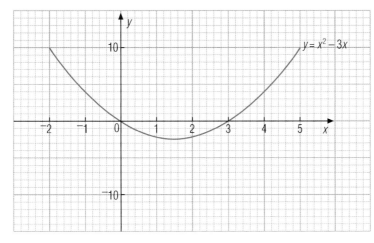

For the curve,
    a) find the value of y when **(i)** $x = 2$ **(ii)** $x = {}^-1$
    b) find the value of x when $y = 7$.

Exercise 9.1B cont'd

4 The curve drawn on the graph is $y = 4 - x^2$.

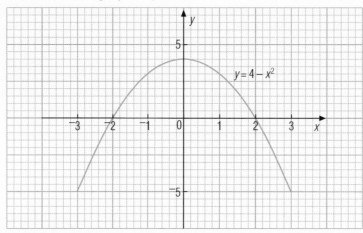

For the curve
  a) find the value of y when **(i)** $x = 2$ **(ii)** $x = 0$
  b) find the value of x when $y = 3$.

5 Two graphs are drawn on the grid, $y = x^2 - 5x + 2$ and $y = 3 - 2x$.

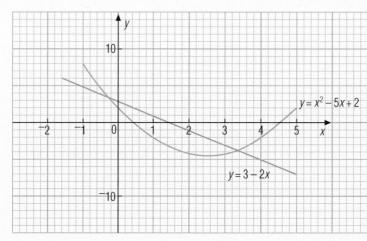

a) For the curve $y = x^2 - 5x + 2$, find the values of x when $y = {}^-2$.
b) Find the coordinates where $y = 3 - 2x$ and $y = x^2 - 5x + 2$ cross

Travel graphs

On a distance–time graph the time is always on the horizontal axis, with the distance on the vertical axis. Care needs to be taken with the scale on the horizontal axis because there are 60 minutes in an hour.

This graph shows the distance from a point A in kilometres, and the time on the 24-hour clock.

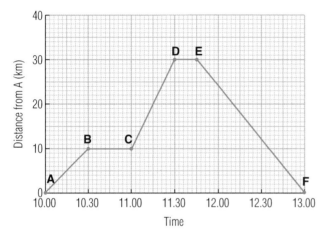

The meanings of the different lines on this distance–time graph are as follows.

A to B shows that 10 km are travelled away from A in 30 minutes at a constant speed.

B to C shows that no distance is covered in the next 30 minutes so it could mean that the driver is resting, or a train is stopping for 30 minutes, or something similar is happening.

C to D shows that 20 km more are travelled away from A in the next 30 minutes at a constant speed.

You can see that the speed is greater between C and D than between A and B because a longer distance is travelled in the same time. You can also see that the line is steeper, which tells you the same thing – that the speed is greater.

D to E shows there is again no movement for 15 minutes.

E to F shows that a distance of 30 km is travelled back towards A in 1 hour and 15 minutes at a constant speed.

You will be asked questions about graphs like this. In most cases the graph will tell a story and you may need to interpret what is happening.

EXAMPLE 3

This distance–time graph shows Maurice's journey from Millfield to Beachold.

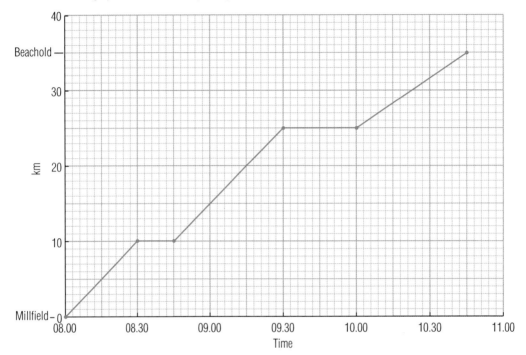

Use the graph to answer these questions.

a) How far is it from Millfield to Beachold?

b) How far does Maurice travel altogether?

c) At what time does Maurice arrive at Beachold?

d) How long does he stop for on the way?

e) What is the speed for the first part of the journey?

a) Millfield to Beachold is 35 km.

b) Maurice travels 35 km.

c) 10.45

d) 45 minutes

e) 20 km per hour.

He stops twice but never goes back towards Millfield, so he travels just the 35 km.

Each 1 cm is equal to 15 minutes.

He stops for 15 minutes and then for another 30 minutes.

Maurice goes 10 km in 30 minutes, so 20 km in one hour.

EXAMPLE 4

This graph shows Sophie's car journey from Barnsley and back.

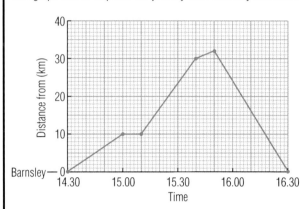

Use the graph to answer these questions.

a) What is the greatest distance that Sophie gets from Barnsley?

b) What is the time when she is at this place?

c) How long does she stop for on the journey?

d) Which is the fastest part of the journey?

a) 32 km

b) 1550

c) 10 minutes

d) The return part.

Each 1 mm is equal to 1 km.

Each 1 cm is equal to 20 minutes.

This is the steepest line, so the fastest speed.

The first thing to do with a distance–time graph is to check the time scale and make sure you know what each small square represents.

Horizontal lines mean no movement.

You cannot have vertical lines.

The steeper the line, the faster the person or vehicle is travelling.

The speed is worked out by finding how far has been travelled in one hour.

A straight line sloping upwards from left to right means that the person is moving away at a constant speed and a straight line sloping downwards from left to right means that the person is moving back towards the starting point at a constant speed.

When you are drawing a distance–time graph, and unless you are told otherwise, assume that any movement is at a steady speed between two points.

EXAMPLE 5

Trudy left home at 8 a.m. and walked 300 m to the bus stop in 5 minutes.

She then had an 8-minute wait for the bus.

She caught the bus and it took 6 minutes to travel the 1·2 km to the school stop.

She got off and slowly walked the 100 m to school in a further 4 minutes.

a) Draw a distance–time graph to illustrate this story. Show time from 8 a.m. to 8.30 a.m. and use a scale of 2 cm for 10 minutes. Show distance from 0 to 3 km and use a scale of 2 cm for 1 km.

b) At what time did she arrive at school?

a)

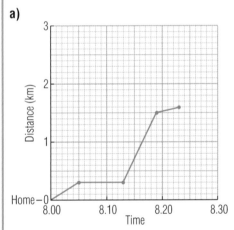

5 minutes is five small squares horizontally. 300 m is 0·3 km so it is three small squares vertically.

8 minutes' wait means eight squares horizontal, i.e. to square 13 horizontally.

1·2 km in 6 minutes means move six square horizontally and 12 vertically, i.e. to square 19 horizontally and 15 vertically.

100 m in 4 minutes means move four squares horizontally and one vertically, i.e. to square 23 horizontally and 16 vertically.

b) She arrived at school at 8.23 a.m.

EXAMPLE 6

Jean walked 6 km in two hours. What was her speed in km per hour?

Speed = distance in one hour = 6 ÷ 2 = 3 km per hour.

EXERCISE 9.2A

1 Tony and Margaret went on a 10 km walk from Tankersley to Warncliffe Side. This graph shows their journey. Use it to answer these questions.

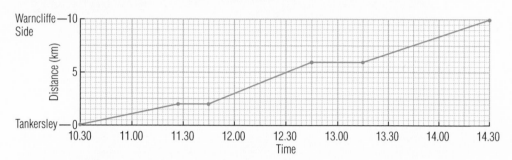

a) How far did they walk before having their first rest?

b) What was the time when they stopped for this rest?

c) How long did they rest for altogether (in both stops)?

d) At what time did they arrive at Warncliffe Side?

2 Brenda walked from home to her friend Sybil's house. This graph shows her journey. Use it to answer these questions.

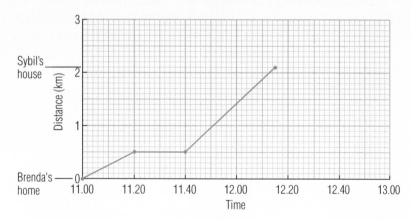

a) How far did she walk?

b) At what time did she arrive at Sybil's house?

c) How long did she stop for on the way?

d) On which part of the journey did she walk more quickly?

Exercise 9.2A cont'd

3 This graph shows Nasreen's walk from home one day and her return on the bus. Use it to answer these questions.

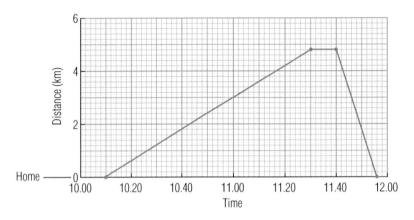

a) At what time did Nasreen leave home?

b) How far did she walk?

c) How long did she stop for?

d) How long did the bus journey take?

4 This graph shows the journeys of Pauline and Scott. Pauline drove from junction 29 of the M1, stopped at the service area at A and continued south. Scott drove from junction 21, also stopped at the services and continued north. Use the graph to answer these questions.

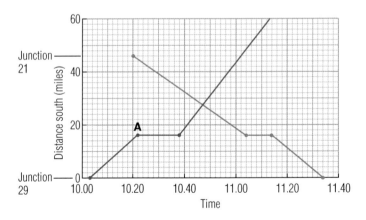

Exercise 9.2A cont'd

    a) At what time did Pauline leave junction 29?

    b) How far is it between the two junctions?

    c) How long did Pauline stop at the service area?

    d) What time was it when Scott and Pauline passed?

    e) (i) Who drove at the fastest speed for part of the journey?

       (ii) For which part of their journey did they drive at this speed?

5 Mr Jenkins left home at 7.15 a.m. and walked the 500 m to the station in 10 minutes. He then waited for the train which left at 7.46 a.m.

    The train took 10 minutes to cover the 12 km to the next station, where Mr Jenkins got off. He then took at taxi for 2 km to his office, taking 8 minutes.

    a) Draw a distance–time graph to show this journey. Show time from 7 a.m. to 8.40 a.m. and use a scale of 2 cm for 20 minutes. Show distance from 0 to 15 km and use a scale of 2 cm for 5 km.

    b) Use your graph to answer these questions.

       (i) How long did Mr Jenkins wait at the station?

       (ii) At what time did he arrive at his office?

    c) At what was the speed of the train over the journey?

6 A car travels 120 miles in 3 hours. What is the speed in miles per hour?

7 A man on an exercise bike rides 8 km in 20 minutes at a steady speed. What is this speed in kilometres per hour?

8 A plane flies 1200 miles in 3 hours. What is its speed in miles per hour?

EXERCISE 9.2B

1   Chris left home and went for a walk, stopping at the supermarket on the way
    and ending at his brother's house. This graph shows his journey. Use it to
    answer these questions.

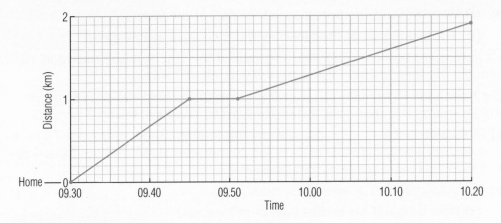

a) At what time did Chris reach the supermarket?
b) How long did he stop at the supermarket?
c) How far was it from his house to his brother's?
d) On which part of the walk did he walk faster?
e) What was his speed on the first part of his journey?

2   This graph shows Baljit's cycle ride. Use the graph to answer these questions.

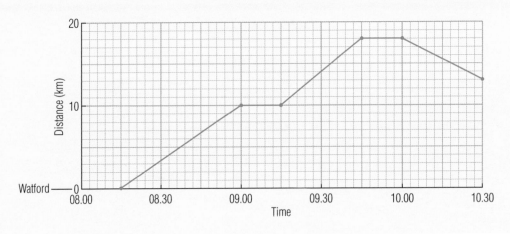

Exercise 9.2B cont'd

a) At what time did Baljit set off from Watford?

b) How long did he rest for?

c) What was the furthest he went from Watford?

d) How far did he ride altogether?

3 Jasmin and Patrick went on a walk. They left home at 9.30 a.m. and walked for 2 miles away from there in 45 minutes. They then sat down for 15 minutes. They continued away from home for another 1·5 miles in the next 30 minutes. They then had another rest for 15 minutes. They returned directly home and arrived there at 1.00 p.m.

a) Draw a distance–time graph to show this journey.

Show time from 9.30 a.m. to 1.00 p.m. and use a scale of 2 cm for 30 minutes.

Show distance from 0 to 4 miles and use a scale of 2 cm for 2 miles.

b) Use your graph to answer these questions.

  (i) How far did they walk altogether?

  (ii) How long did it take them to walk back from the furthest point?

4 This graph shows Netty's ride on her scooter. Use the graph to answer these questions.

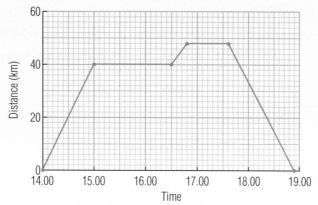

a) How long did Netty stop for the first time?

b) What was her furthest distance from her starting point?

c) When did she arrive at the furthest distance?

d) How long did she take to ride back?

e) What was her speed on her return journey?

Exercise 9.2B cont'd

5 This graph shows the journeys of two men, Brian and Malcolm, who both left Leeds. Brian left first. Use the graph to answer these questions.

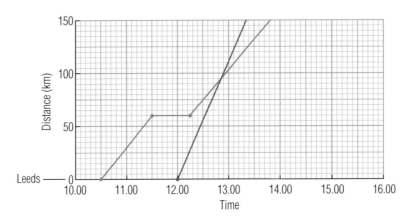

a) How much later than Brian did Malcolm leave?

b) How long did Brian stop for?

c) How far had they travelled when Malcolm passed Brian?

d) At what time did Malcolm pass Brian?

6 A train travels 65 km in 30 minutes. What is its speed in kilometres per hour?

7 A snail creeps 400 cm in 10 seconds. What is its speed in centimetres per second?

8 Joan runs 9 miles in 2 hours. What is her speed in miles per hour?

ACTIVITY 2

Draw a graph with straight lines only, to show the following journeys.

a) your journey to school

b) a car travelling on a motorway to the nearest city along a clear road

c) a car travelling along the M25 during a busy period

d) a shopping trip to a supermarket outside town

e) a train travelling along a fast stretch between two cities

f) a ferry crossing the English Channel

g) a hiker walking in the Lake District, first along a flat piece of terrain and then up a very steep slope.

Other graphs and tables representing real data

You have already looked at bar charts and pictograms, and these may be referred to here.

However, the main emphasis is on interpreting line graphs of real data and realising when the graphs are misleading.

This shows the cost of circular wall plates of different radius.

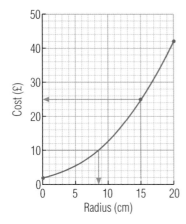

Use the graph to find out

a) the cost of a plate of radius 15 cm

b) the radius of a plate that costs £10.

a) £25

b) 8·5 cm.

> In both cases the answer is not easy to give very accurately. Any answer between **a)** £24 and £26 and **b)** 8 and 9 cm would be acceptable.

There can be various reasons for graphs being misleading. The most common is that the vertical axis does not start at zero when it should do.

EXAMPLE 8

This bar chart shows the percentage support for Labour, Conservative and Lib-Dems in Staffield.

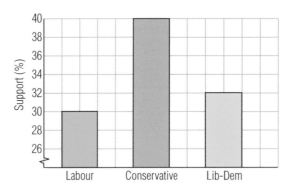

Explain why the diagram is misleading.

By not having the vertical scale starting at zero, it makes it appear that the Conservatives have over twice the support of either of the others. Careful reading of the scales shows that the support for the three is

Labour 28%   Conservative 40%   Llb-Dem 32%

Graphs can also be misleading when they are three-dimensional, and sometimes when it is assumed that intermediate points have meaning when they do not.

EXERCISE 9.3A

1

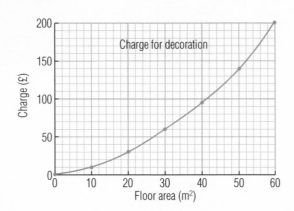

This graph shows the charge that George makes for decorating rooms with different floor areas.

a) What does he charge for a room with floor area **(i)** 20 m² **(ii)** 50 m²?

b) George says he will charge £100 to decorate Bill's room. What is the floor area of Bill's room?

2 This table shows the distances in miles between various towns in Wales.

	Cardiff	Carmarthen	Neath	Newport	Swansea
Cardiff	X	64	36	91	41
Carmarthen	64	X	30	29	27
Neath	36	30	X	58	10
Newport	91	29	58	X	55
Swansea	41	27	10	55	X

a) How far is it from **(i)** Newport to Swansea **(ii)** Cardiff to Neath?

b) Morgan drove from Cardiff to Swansea to Carmarthen and then back to Cardiff. How far did he drive altogether?

Exercise 9.3A cont'd

3 The graph shows Diane's height between the ages of 1 and 5.

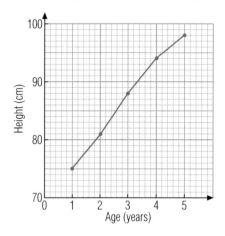

a) What was her height at **(i)** 4 years old   **(ii)** $2\frac{1}{2}$ years old?

b) Estimate her age when she was 90 cm tall.

4 This diagram shows the sales figures in £100 000 for the years 1990 to 1995.

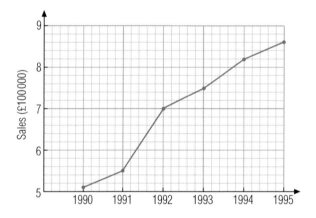

a) What were the sales figures for 1994?

b) By how much did the figures increase between 1991 and 1992?

c) The sales director says that the graph shows that the figures more than doubled between 1991 and 1992. Why is this statement wrong, and why does the graph make it appear true?

Exercise 9.3A cont'd

5 The graph shows the cost of hiring a car for the day from two different firms.

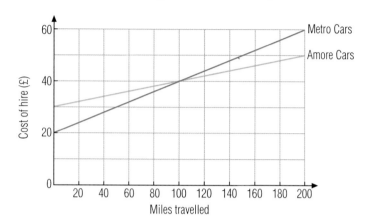

a) How much does it cost to hire a car from Metro Cars if you travel 160 miles?

b) How much does it cost to hire a car from Amore Cars if you travel 60 miles?

c) David wishes to hire a car for the day and expects to travel 120 miles. Which firm is cheaper and by how much?

EXERCISE 9.3B

1 This diagram shows the speed of a car over the first 6 seconds after setting off.

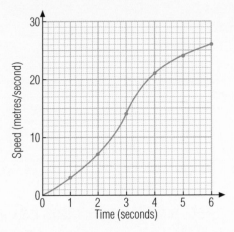

a) What is the car's speed after **(i)** 3 seconds **(ii)** 4·8 seconds?

b) How long after the start will the car's speed be
(i) 7 metres/second **(ii)** 20 metres/second?

2 The chart shows the temperature at noon on the seven days in the week of the North Yorks Show.

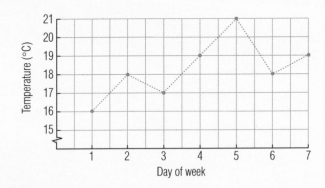

a) Which day was the hottest and what was that temperature?

b) Between which two days was there the biggest drop in temperature?

c) Wayne said that the temperature after $3\frac{1}{2}$ days was 18 °C. Why was this wrong?

Exercise 9.3B cont'd

3 This graph shows the temperature of water heating in a kettle.

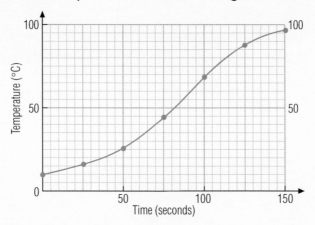

a) What was the temperature after **(i)** 75 seconds   **(ii)** 110 seconds?

b) How long did it take to reach   **(i)** 50 °C   **(ii)** 85 °C?

4 The publicity department at Farrow Bay drew this bar chart to show the average hours of sunshine in June in Farrow Bay, Pascal Cove, Montron Cliff and Duncan Sands.

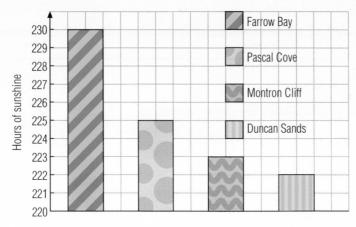

a) What is wrong with the chart and what does it suggest to the person looking at it?

b) How many hours of extra sun does Farrow Bay get compared with Montron Cliff?

Exercise 9.3B cont'd

5 This graph shows the charge for tiling by Mr. Darley and by Mr. Metcalf.

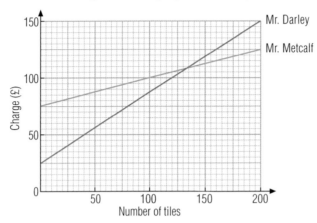

a) How much does Mr Darley charge to tile a room needing
(i) 50 **(ii)** 175 tiles?

b) How much does Mr Metcalf charge to tile a room needing
(i) 50 **(ii)** 175 tiles?

c) Mrs Timmis wants a room to be tiled with 150 tiles. Who is cheaper, and by how much?

Key ideas

- When reading a graph always check the scale.
- All distance–time graphs have the time on the horizontal and the distance on the vertical axis.
- A horizontal line on a distance–line graph indicates no movement.
- The most common misleading feature of a graph is to have a vertical axis which starts above zero when the comparative heights are important.

10 Factors and multiples

You should already know

- how to multiply and divide by all single-digit numbers.

Patterns for numbers

20 can be shown as

. . . .

one row of 20 dots

. . . .
. . . .

2 rows of 10 dots

or

. . . . .
. . . . .
. . . . .
. . . . .

4 rows of 5 dots.

This shows that $20 = 1 \times 20 = 2 \times 10 = 4 \times 5$.

So 1, 2, 4, 5, 10 and 20 will all divide exactly into 20.

So 1, 2, 4, 5, 10 and 20 are all **factors** of 20.

The factors of a number are all the
numbers that will divide exactly into it.

Exam tip

The factors of any number
always include 1 and the
number itself. For example 1 and
20 are two of the factors of 20.

EXAMPLE 1

a) Draw all the rectangular (and square) patterns that you can for
   (i) 16   **(ii)** 27.
b) Write down the product that each pattern shows.
c) Write down all the factors of
   (i) 16   **(ii)** 27.

a)

   (i)

or

or

(ii)

or

b) (i) $16 = 1 \times 16 = 2 \times 8 = 4 \times 4$
   (ii) $27 = 1 \times 27 = 3 \times 9$
c) (i) Factors are 1, 2, 4, 8, 16.
   (ii) Factors are 1, 3, 9, 27.

Sometimes you will just want to write down the factors without drawing the patterns. To do this you need to see if the number will divide exactly, first by 2 then by 3, and so forth.

EXAMPLE 2

For the numbers 4, 5, 8, 11, 14, 17 and 20, find which has a factor of

a) 2   **b)** 5

a) 4, 8, 14, 20   [4 ÷ 2 = 2] yes, [5 ÷ 2 = 2·5] no etc.

b) 5, 20   [4 ÷ 5 = 0·8] no, [5 ÷ 5 = 1] yes etc.

Exam tip

When testing for factors, keep trying until the result is smaller than the number you are trying.

EXAMPLE 3

Find all the factors of **a)** 8   **b)** 11   **c)** 30.

a) 8 = 1 × 8   All will be divisible by 1. Now try 2.

     = 2 × 4

Factors of 8 are 1, 2, 4, 8.   Now try 3 [8 ÷ 3 = 2·66]. It won't work. The answer is smaller than the number you are trying, so you need not go any further.

b) 11 = 1 × 11

Factors of 11 are 1 and 11.   Now try 2 [11 ÷ 2 = 5·5]. It won't work. Now 3 [11 ÷ 3 = 3·33]. It won't work. Now 4 [11 ÷ 4 = 2·75]. It won't work. The answer is smaller than the number you are trying, so you need not go any further.

c) 30 = 1 × 30   Now try 2.

     = 2 × 15   Now try 3.

     = 3 × 10   Now try 4 [30 ÷ 4 = 7·5]. It won't work.

     = 5 × 6   Now try 5.

No point in trying more as 6 has already been found and it would give 5, which is smaller.

Factors of 30 are 1, 2, 3, 5, 6, 10, 15, 30.

ACTIVITY 1

Pairing factors.

In Example 3 the factors of 30 were 1, 2, 3, 5, 6, 10, 15 and 30.

These were all pairs 1×30, 2×15, 3×10, 5×6.

a) Try this paring for the numbers 18, 24, 40.

b) Now try these 9, 16, 25. What do you notice? What type of numbers are these?

Exam tip

The factors of any numbers always include 1 and the number itself. For example, 1 and 20 are two of the factors of 20.

Exam tip

Pairing factors often helps you to write them down.

EXERCISE 10.1A

1 a) Draw all the rectangular (and square) patterns that you can, and write down the product that each pattern shows, for

    (i) 15   **(ii)** 24

  b) Write down all the factors of **(i)** 15   **(ii)** 24.

2 For the numbers 3, 8, 12, 16, 21, find which has a factor of

  a) 3

  b) 4.

3 For the numbers 13, 19, 36, 45 and 81, find which has a factor of

  a) 3

  b) 12.

4 Is 73 a factor of **a)** 365 **b)** 651 **c)** 1095?

5 Find all the factors of

  a) 3 **b)** 6 **c)** 12 **d)** 17 **e)** 25 **f)** 34 **g)** 41 **h)** 60 **i)** 92 **j)** 140.

EXERCISE 10.1B

1 **a)** Draw all the rectangular (and square) patterns that you can, and write down the product that each pattern shows, for
   (i) 18   **(ii)** 20
   b) Write down all the factors of **(i)** 18   **(ii)** 20.

2 For the numbers 6, 10, 15, 19, 24, find which has a factor of
   a) 3
   b) 4.

3 For the numbers 23, 30 38, 45, 81, find which has a factor of
   a) 2
   b) 9.

4 Is 62 a factor of **a)** 366   **b)** 434   **c)** 744?

5 Find all the factors of
   a) 4   **b)** 7   **c)** 14   **d)** 19   **e)** 35   **f)** 40   **g)** 49   **h)** 61   **i)** 95   **j)** 234.

Common factors

As the name suggests common factors are factors that are common to more than one number.

EXAMPLE 4

a) Find the factors of **(i)** 12   **(ii)** 24   **(iii)** 36.
b) Write down the common factors of 12, 24 and 36 that are greater than 1.

a) (i) $12 = 1 \times 12 = 2 \times 6 = 3 \times 4$
   Factors are 1, 2, 3, 4, 6, 12.
   (ii) $24 = 1 \times 24 = 2 \times 12 = 3 \times 8 = 4 \times 6$ Testing shows 5 is not a factor.
   Factors are 1, 2, 3, 4, 6, 12, 14.
   (iii) $36 = 1 \times 36 = 2 \times 18 = 3 \times 12 = 4 \times 9 = 6 \times 6$.   Testing shows 5 is not a factor.
   Factors are 1, 2, 3, 4, 6, 9, 12, 18, 36.

b) Common factors of 12, 24 and 36 greater than 1 are 2, 3, 4, 6, 12.

Sometimes you may be asked for the highest common factor. In Example 4 you can see that the highest common factor of 12, 24 and 36 is 12.

> ### Exam tip
> All numbers have 1 as a factor so normally you will be asked for the common factors greater than 1. If you are just asked for the common factors you must include 1.

EXAMPLE 5

a) Find the common factors of 70 and 105.

b) Write down the highest common factor of 70 and 105.

a) $70 = 1 \times 70 = 2 \times 35 = 5 \times 14 = 7 \times 10$

Factors are 1, 2, 5, 7, 10, 14, 35, 70

Tests for 3 and 4 do not work.

Tests for 6, 8 and 9 do not work.

$105 = 1 \times 105 = 3 \times 35 = 5 \times 21 = 7 \times 15$

Factors are 1, 3, 5, 7, 15, 21, 35, 105.

Tests for 2 and 4 do not work.

Tests for 6, 8, 9 and 10 do not work.

The common factors are 1, 5, 7, 35.

b) The highest common factor of 70 and 105 is 35.

EXAMPLE 6

For the numbers 6, 12, 16, 24.

a) Is 2 a common factor?

b) Is 3 a common factor?

c) Is 6 a common factor?

a) 2 is a common factor.   **They are all even.**

b) 3 is not a common factor.   **It is not a factor of 16.**

c) 6 is not a common factor.   **It is not a factor of 16.**

> **Exam tip**
>
> When testing for factors, if 2 is not a factor, then none of the other even numbers will be a factor and you do not need to test them.

EXERCISE 10.2A

1 **a)** Find the factors of **(i)** 8   **(ii)** 12   **(iii)** 16.
   b) Write down the common factors of 8, 12 and 16.

2 **a)** Find the factors of **(i)** 12   **(ii)** 24   **(iii)** 30.
   b) Write down the common factors of 12, 24 and 30 that are bigger than 1.

3 **a)** Find the common factors of 28 and 42 that are greater than 1.
   b) Write down the highest common factor of 28 and 42.

4 For the numbers 18, 24, 36, which of the following are common factors?
   a) 2   **b)** 3   **c)** 5

5 **a)** Find the common factors of 16 and 36 that are greater than 1.
   b) Write down the highest common factor of 16 and 36.

6 Look at these numbers: 2, 5, 9, 12, 23, 25.
   a) Which have a factor of 2?
   b) Which have a factor of 5?

7 Look at these numbers: 2, 3, 4, 5, 6, 9, 12.
   Write down the ones that are
   a) odd numbers   **b)** factors of 24   **c)** multiples of 3.

8 Look at these numbers: 12, 15, 18, 20, 21, 25
   Write down the ones that are
   a) multiples of 2   **b)** factors of 100
   c) multiples of 3   **d)** multiples of 5.

EXERCISE 10.2B

1 **a)** Find the factors of **(i)** 15   **(ii)** 30   **(iii)** 45.
   b) Write down the common factors of 15, 30 and 45.

2 **a)** Find the factors of **(i)** 20   **(ii)** 30   **(iii)** 50.
   b) Write down the common factors of 20, 30 and 50 that are bigger than 1.

3 **a)** Find the common factors of 48 and 64 that are greater than 1.
   b) Write down the highest common factor of 48 and 64.

4 For the numbers 15, 20, 25, which of the following are common factors.
   a) 2   **b)** 3   **c)** 5?

5 **a)** Find the common factors of 21 and 63 that are greater than 1.
   c) Write down the highest common factor of 21 and 63.

6 Look at these numbers: 1, 4, 8, 11, 22, 25, 29.
   a) Which have a factor of 2?
   b) Which have a factor of 5?

7 Look at these numbers: 3, 5, 6, 8, 9, 10.
   Write down the ones that are
   a) even numbers   **b)** factors of 24   **c)** multiples of 5.

8 Look at these numbers: 8, 10, 12, 16, 18, 20, 24, 28.
   Write down the ones that are
   a) multiples of 4
   b) multiples of 3
   c) multiples of 12.
   d) Describe any connection you see between the answers to **a)**, **b)** and **c)**

Multiples

A multiple of a number is any number that the number will divide into exactly.

For instance the multiples of 2 are 2, 4, 6, 8, 10 ...

In a way they are the opposites of factors, but there is an infinite number of them for each number.

EXAMPLE 8

Write down five multiples of 3.

3, 6, 9, 12, 15   **This is one answer but there are many different ones.**

15, 30, 36, 45, 60   **This is another correct answer.**

EXAMPLE 9

Write down all the multiples of 6 that are less than 28.

6, 12, 18, 24   **Remember that 6 is a multiple of 6.**

Common multiples

A number that is a multiple of both n and m is called a common multiple of n and m.

EXAMPLE 10

a) Write down the first 5 multiples of
   (i) 3   **(ii)** 4.
b) Which of these multiples are common to 3 and 4?

a) (i) 3, 6, 9, 12, 15   **(ii)** 4, 8, 12, 16, 20
b) The only common multiple of 3 and 4 in this list is 12.

EXAMPLE 11

Find three common multiples of 4 and 6.

Multiples of 4 are

4, 8, 12, 16, 24, 28, 32, 36, …

Write out as many as you think you need and if necessary add more.

Multiples of 6 are

6, 12, 18, 24, 30, 36, …

Three common multiples of 4 and 6 are 12, 24, and 36.

Sometimes you will be asked for the lowest common multiple. In Example 11 you can see that the lowest common multiple of 4 and 6 is 12.

Exam tip

There is an infinite number of multiples of any number and an infinite number of common multiples of any group of numbers.

EXAMPLE 12

Find the lowest common multiple of 3, 4 and 6.

Multiples of 3 are

3, 6, 9, 12, 15, 18, 21, 24

As before, list as many as you think you need and add more if necessary.

Multiples of 4 are

4, 8, 12, 16, 20, 24, 28

In these lists there are just two common multiples of 12 and 24.

You can see that the lowest common multiple is 12.

Multiples of 6 are

6, 12, 18, 24

So the lowest common multiple is 12.

EXERCISE 10.3A

1   Write down any two multiples of **a)** 4   **b)** 5   **c)** 15   **d)** 50   **e)** 65.
2   Write down the first five multiples of **a)** 3   **b)** 5   **c)** 8   **d)** 10   **e)** 12.
3   Find three common multiples of **a)** 2 and 3   **b)** 6 and 8.
4   **a)** Write down the first five multiples of **(i)** 2   **(ii)** 5   **(iii)** 6   **(iv)** 9.
    b) Find the lowest common multiple of **(i)** 2 and 5   **(ii)** 2 and 6   **(iii)** 6 and 9.
5   Find the lowest common multiple of
    a) 2, 3 and 4   **b)** 2, 5 and 6   **c)** 4, 8 and 16   **d)** 2, 5, 10 and 15.
6   Look at the numbers 12, 13, 14, 15, 17, 21. Write down which are
    a) multiples of 2   **b)** multiples of 3   **c)** multiples of 5   **d)** multiples of 7.

EXERCISE 10.3B

1   Write down any two multiples of **a)** 11   **b)** 17   **c)** 22   **d)** 40   **e)** 55.
2   Write down the first five multiples of **a)** 2   **b)** 6   **c)** 7   **d)** 15   **e)** 20.
3   Find three common multiples of **a)** 2 and 7   **b)** 3 and 9.
4   **a)** Write down the first five multiples of **(i)** 2   **(ii)** 8   **(iii)** 9   **(iv)** 12.
    b) Find the lowest common multiple of **(i)** 2 and 8   **(ii)** 9 and 12   **(iv)** 8 and 12.
5   Find the lowest common multiple of
    a) 3, 5 and 6   **b)** 2, 4, and 7   **c)** 2, 3, and 8   **d)** 3, 4, 5 and 15.
6   Look at the numbers 24, 33, 34, 45, 57, 60, 61. Write down which are
    a) multiples of 2   **b)** multiples of 3   **c)** multiples of 5
    d) multiples of 7   **e)** prime numbers.

Key ideas

- A factor of the number n is any number that divides exactly into m.
- To find common factors, list all the factors and choose the common ones.
- To find the highest common factor, find all the common factors and choose the highest.
- A multiple of n is any number that n divides into exactly.
- To find the lowest common multiple of n and m, list the multiples of each in order (smallest first) until one that is common appears.

Chapter 10 *Factors and multiples*

11 Using simple fractions

You should already know

- how to add and subtract, multiply and divide single digits.

Fractions on scales

Old rulers used to be marked like this scale with each whole unit (inch) split into $\frac{1}{2}$, $\frac{1}{4}$ and $\frac{1}{8}$.

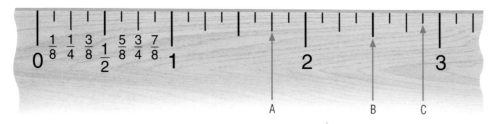

The points marked are A $1\frac{3}{4}$, B $2\frac{1}{2}$ and C $2\frac{7}{8}$

Exam tip

Numbers over one, e.g. $2\frac{1}{2}$, can have a whole-number part and a fraction part. These are often called 'mixed numbers'.

EXAMPLE 1

a) On the scale below what are the points marked A, B and C?
b) Make a copy of the scale and mark the points D $\frac{5}{8}$, E1$\frac{1}{2}$, F2$\frac{3}{4}$.

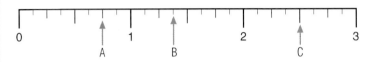

a) A $\frac{3}{4}$, B 1$\frac{3}{8}$ and C 2$\frac{1}{2}$.
b)

From the scale you can see that
two $\frac{1}{8}$s are the same as $\frac{1}{4}$
two $\frac{1}{4}$s are the same as $\frac{1}{2}$
two $\frac{1}{2}$s are the same as 1.
You can also use the scale to add and subtract fractions.

EXAMPLE 2

Use a scale from 2 to 5 to find 2$\frac{1}{2}$ + 1$\frac{5}{8}$.

The scale drawn here has been started at 2 as you do not need anything below that.

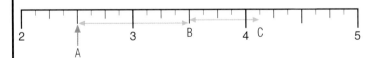

2$\frac{1}{2}$ is marked A. Then adding one whole unit brings us to B, and with five divisions of $\frac{1}{8}$ we arrive at C.

The answer is at C 4$\frac{1}{8}$.
So 2$\frac{1}{2}$ + 1$\frac{5}{8}$ = 4$\frac{1}{8}$.

EXAMPLE 3

Use a scale marked from 0 to 4 to find $3\frac{1}{4} - 1\frac{7}{8}$.

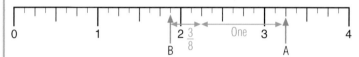

$3\frac{1}{4}$ is marked A and $1\frac{7}{8}$ is marked B.

One whole unit and then $\frac{3}{8}$ are counted between them.

So $3\frac{1}{4} - 1\frac{7}{8} = 1\frac{3}{8}$.

> **There are two ways to do this. One is to mark both of these numbers and count the difference. The other is to mark the first and count the second backwards to find the answer. The first method is used here.**

EXERCISE 11.1A

1 Write down the value on the scale of A, B, C and D.

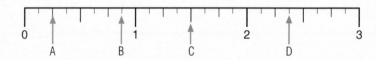

2 Write down the value on the scale of A, B, C and D.

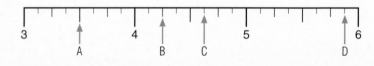

Exercise 11.1A cont'd

3 Draw a scale from 0 to 3 and mark the points A $\frac{1}{2}$, B $1\frac{7}{8}$, C $2\frac{1}{8}$, D $2\frac{3}{4}$.

4 Draw a scale from 2 to 5 and mark the points A $2\frac{1}{8}$, B $3\frac{3}{8}$, C $4\frac{1}{2}$, D $4\frac{3}{4}$.

5 Draw scales from 0 to 4 and use them to work out these additions and subtractions.

a) $\frac{3}{4} + \frac{1}{2}$ **b)** $\frac{5}{8} + 1\frac{1}{4}$ **c)** $2\frac{1}{8} + 1\frac{1}{2}$ **d)** $1\frac{1}{2} + 1\frac{5}{8}$ **e)** $2\frac{1}{8} + \frac{7}{8}$

f) $\frac{7}{8} - \frac{1}{2}$ **g)** $3\frac{1}{2} - 1\frac{1}{4}$ **h)** $2\frac{1}{4} - 1\frac{3}{8}$ **i)** $3\frac{1}{8} - 1\frac{1}{4}$ **j)** $3\frac{5}{8} - \frac{7}{8}$

EXERCISE 11.1B

1 Write down the value on the scale of A, B, C and D.

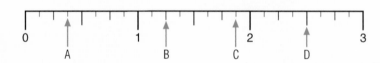

2 Write down the value on the scale of A, B, C and D.

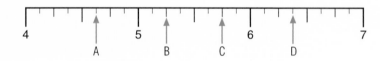

3 Draw a scale from 0 to 3 and mark the points A $\frac{1}{4}$, B $\frac{5}{8}$, C $2\frac{3}{8}$, D $2\frac{1}{4}$.

4 Draw a scale from 2 to 5 and mark the points A $2\frac{7}{8}$, B $3\frac{1}{8}$, C $4\frac{1}{4}$, D $4\frac{5}{8}$.

5 Draw scales from 0 to 4 and use them to work out these additions and subtractions.

a) $\frac{3}{8} + \frac{1}{4}$ **b)** $\frac{5}{8} + 1\frac{1}{2}$ **c)** $2\frac{3}{8} + 1\frac{1}{2}$ **d)** $1\frac{3}{8} + 1\frac{5}{8}$ **e)** $2\frac{1}{8} + \frac{1}{4}$

f) $\frac{5}{8} - \frac{1}{4}$ **g)** $2\frac{1}{2} - \frac{3}{8}$ **h)** $3\frac{3}{8} - 1\frac{3}{4}$ **i)** $3\frac{1}{4} - 1\frac{3}{8}$ **j)** $3\frac{3}{8} - 1\frac{5}{8}$

Chapter 11 *Using simple fractions*

Addition of fractions

Look at this diagram.
$\frac{3}{8}$ has been shaded.

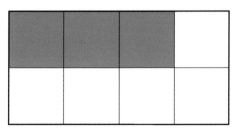

Now another $\frac{2}{8}$ has been shaded.

So altogether $\frac{5}{8}$ has been shaded.

This means that $\frac{3}{8} + \frac{2}{8} = \frac{5}{8}$.

This shows you the method of adding fractions.

The bottom numbers (denominators) must be the same. You then simply add the top numbers (numerators) and leave the bottom numbers the same.

EXAMPLE 4

Work out $\frac{1}{4} + \frac{2}{4}$

$\frac{1}{4} + \frac{2}{4} = \frac{3}{4}$ Add the 'tops' and leave the 'bottoms' the same.

You can use equivalent fractions to add fractions which do not have the same bottom number.

Equivalent fractions

Look at these diagrams.

$\frac{1}{4}$ has been shaded.

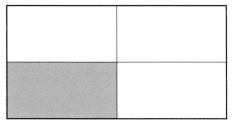

$\frac{2}{8}$ has been shaded.

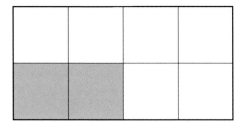

In each case the same amount has been shaded.

This shows that $\frac{1}{4} = \frac{2}{8}$. These are called equivalent fractions.

To form equivalent fractions you multiply the top and bottom numbers by the same amount, or you divide the top and bottom numbers by the same amount.

For example

$$\overset{\times 2}{\underset{\times 2}{\frac{3}{4} \quad \frac{6}{8}}} \qquad \overset{\div 4}{\underset{\div 4}{\frac{4}{8} \quad \frac{1}{2}}}$$

The second example above is often called 'cancelling'. It gives the fraction 'in its simplest form' or 'in its lowest terms'.

EXAMPLE 5

Work out $\frac{3}{8} + \frac{1}{4}$

First change $\frac{1}{4}$ into eighths by multiplying 'top' and 'bottom' by 2.

$\frac{3}{8} + \frac{1}{4} = \frac{3}{8} + \frac{2}{8} = \frac{5}{8}$

EXAMPLE 6

Work out $\frac{3}{4} + \frac{5}{8}$

$\frac{3}{4} + \frac{5}{8} = \frac{6}{8} + \frac{5}{8} = \frac{11}{8}$

First change $\frac{3}{4}$ into eighths by multiplying 'top' and 'bottom' by 2.

$\frac{11}{8} = 1\frac{3}{8}$.

This answer is an improper (top-heavy) fraction. You should change it to a mixed number.

EXAMPLE 7

Work out $2\frac{1}{2} + 3\frac{1}{4}$.

$2 + 3 = 5$

Work out the whole numbers first.

$\frac{1}{2} + \frac{1}{4} = \frac{2}{4} + \frac{1}{4} = \frac{3}{4}$

Then work out the fractions.

The answer is therefore $5\frac{3}{4}$.

This is often set out in the following way.

$2\frac{1}{2} + 3\frac{1}{4} = 5\frac{2+1}{4} = 5\frac{3}{4}$

EXAMPLE 8

Work out $3\frac{3}{4}+\frac{7}{8}$.

$3 + 0 = 3$

$\frac{6}{8} + \frac{7}{8} = \frac{13}{8} = 1\frac{5}{8}$

The answer is therefore $3 + 1\frac{5}{8} = 4\frac{5}{8}$

Work out the whole numbers first.

Then change $\frac{3}{4}$ into eighths by multiplying 'top' and 'bottom' by 2.

Exam tip

It is worth remembering a few common equivalent fractions, for example

$\frac{1}{4} = \frac{2}{8}, \frac{1}{2} = \frac{2}{4} = \frac{4}{8}, \frac{3}{4} = \frac{6}{8}$.

It is also useful to know that

$1 = \frac{8}{8} = \frac{4}{4} = \frac{2}{2}$.

Subtraction of fractions

The method for subtracting fractions is the same as for adding fractions and is shown in the following examples.

EXAMPLE 9

Work out $\frac{5}{8}-\frac{1}{8}$.

$\frac{5}{8} - \frac{1}{8} = \frac{4}{8}$

Subtract the tops and leave the bottom numbers the same.

$\frac{4}{8} = \frac{1}{2}$

Divide top and bottom numbers by 4.

EXAMPLE 10

Work out $\frac{7}{8}-\frac{3}{4}$.

$\frac{7}{8} - \frac{3}{4} = \frac{7}{8} - \frac{6}{8} = \frac{1}{8}$

EXAMPLE 11

Work out $5\frac{3}{4} - 2\frac{3}{8}$.

$5 - 2 = 3$

> **Work out the whole numbers first.**

$\frac{3}{4} - \frac{3}{8} = \frac{6}{8} - \frac{3}{8} = \frac{3}{8}$

> **Then work out the fractions.**

The answer is $3 + \frac{3}{8} = 3\frac{3}{8}$

Or $5\frac{3}{4} - 2\frac{3}{8} = 3\frac{6-3}{8} = 3\frac{3}{8}$

There is one difficult case you may meet when you are subtracting mixed numbers. This is shown in the examples below.

EXAMPLE 12

Work out $1\frac{3}{8} - \frac{3}{4}$.

$1 - 0 = 1$

> **Work out the whole numbers first.**

$\frac{3}{8} - \frac{3}{4} = \frac{3}{8} - \frac{6}{8} = \frac{-3}{8}$

The answer is therefore $1 - \frac{3}{8} = \frac{8}{8} - \frac{3}{8} = \frac{5}{8}$

EXAMPLE 13

Work out $5\frac{1}{2} - 2\frac{7}{8}$.

$5 - 2 = 3$

> **Work out the whole numbers first.**

$\frac{1}{2} - \frac{7}{8} = \frac{4}{8} - \frac{7}{8} = \frac{-3}{8}$

> **Then work out the fractions.**

The answer is therefore $3 - \frac{3}{8} = 2\frac{8}{8} - \frac{3}{8} = 2\frac{5}{8}$.

EXERCISE 11.2A

1 Work out

a) $\frac{1}{8} + \frac{3}{8}$ **b)** $\frac{3}{8} + \frac{3}{8}$ **c)** $\frac{3}{8} + \frac{1}{4}$ **d)** $\frac{1}{8} + \frac{1}{2}$ **e)** $\frac{3}{8} + \frac{1}{2}$

2 Work out

a) $2\frac{1}{8} + \frac{5}{8}$ **b)** $\frac{1}{8} + 2\frac{3}{8}$ **c)** $1\frac{3}{8} - 2\frac{1}{4}$ **d)** $1\frac{5}{8} + \frac{1}{4}$ **e)** $4\frac{3}{8} + 3\frac{1}{2}$

3 Write these top-heavy fractions as mixed numbers.

a) $\frac{11}{8}$ **b)** $\frac{15}{8}$ **c)** $\frac{7}{4}$ **d)** $\frac{5}{2}$ **e)** $\frac{23}{8}$

4 Work out

a) $1\frac{3}{8} + 1\frac{5}{8}$ **b)** $2\frac{5}{8} + \frac{3}{4}$ **c)** $\frac{7}{8} + \frac{1}{4}$ **d)** $2\frac{1}{2} + 3\frac{5}{8}$ **e)** $3\frac{3}{8} + 1\frac{3}{4}$

5 Work out

a) $\frac{7}{8} - \frac{3}{8}$ **b)** $\frac{3}{8} - \frac{3}{8}$ **c)** $\frac{3}{8} - \frac{1}{4}$ **d)** $\frac{5}{8} - \frac{1}{2}$ **e)** $\frac{7}{8} - \frac{1}{2}$

6 Work out

a) $2\frac{7}{8} - \frac{5}{8}$ **b)** $4\frac{5}{8} - 2\frac{3}{8}$ **c)** $1\frac{3}{8} - \frac{1}{4}$ **d)** $1\frac{5}{8} - 1\frac{1}{2}$ **e)** $4\frac{7}{8} - 3\frac{1}{2}$

7 Work out

a) $2\frac{1}{8} - \frac{5}{8}$ **b)** $4\frac{1}{8} - 2\frac{3}{8}$ **c)** $1\frac{3}{8} - \frac{3}{4}$ **d)** $1\frac{1}{8} - \frac{1}{2}$ **e)** $4\frac{3}{8} - 3\frac{1}{2}$

8 Work out

a) $\frac{1}{4} + \frac{1}{2}$ **b)** $\frac{5}{8} + 1\frac{1}{4}$ **c)** $2\frac{1}{8} + 1\frac{1}{2}$ **d)** $1\frac{1}{2} + 1\frac{5}{8}$ **e)** $2\frac{1}{8} + \frac{7}{8}$

f) $\frac{7}{8} - \frac{1}{2}$ **g)** $3\frac{1}{2} - 1\frac{1}{4}$ **h)** $2\frac{1}{4} - 1\frac{3}{8}$ **i)** $3\frac{1}{8} - 1\frac{1}{4}$ **j)** $3\frac{5}{8} - \frac{7}{8}$

EXERCISE 11.2B

1 Work out
   a) $\frac{2}{8} + \frac{3}{8}$ **b)** $\frac{5}{8} + \frac{1}{8}$ **c)** $\frac{1}{8} + \frac{1}{4}$ **d)** $\frac{3}{8} + \frac{1}{2}$ **e)** $\frac{1}{4} + \frac{1}{2}$

2 Work out
   a) $2\frac{1}{8} + \frac{3}{8}$ **b)** $\frac{3}{8} + 2\frac{3}{8}$ **c)** $1\frac{1}{4} + 2\frac{1}{4}$ **d)** $1\frac{3}{8} + \frac{1}{2}$ **e)** $4\frac{1}{8} + 3\frac{1}{2}$

   Write these top-heavy fractions as mixed numbers.

3 **a)** $\frac{10}{8}$ **b)** $\frac{13}{8}$ **c)** $\frac{5}{4}$ **d)** $\frac{7}{2}$ **e)** $\frac{21}{8}$

4 Work out
   a) $1\frac{1}{8} + 1\frac{7}{8}$ **b)** $2\frac{5}{8} + \frac{1}{4}$ **c)** $\frac{7}{8} + \frac{3}{4}$ **d)** $2\frac{3}{4} + 3\frac{5}{8}$ **e)** $3\frac{1}{2} + 1\frac{3}{4}$

5 Work out
   a) $\frac{5}{8} - \frac{3}{8}$ **b)** $\frac{7}{8} - \frac{1}{8}$ **c)** $\frac{3}{4} - \frac{1}{2}$ **d)** $\frac{7}{8} - \frac{1}{2}$ **e)** $\frac{7}{8} - \frac{3}{4}$

6 Work out
   a) $2\frac{7}{8} - \frac{1}{8}$ **b)** $4\frac{5}{8} - 2\frac{1}{2}$ **c)** $3\frac{3}{8} - \frac{1}{4}$ **d)** $1\frac{3}{4} - 1\frac{1}{2}$ **e)** $4\frac{7}{8} - 3\frac{1}{4}$

7 Work out
   a) $2\frac{1}{8} - \frac{3}{8}$ **b)** $4\frac{1}{8} - 2\frac{5}{8}$ **c)** $1\frac{5}{8} - \frac{3}{4}$ **d)** $1\frac{3}{8} - \frac{1}{2}$ **e)** $4\frac{3}{8} - \frac{1}{2}$

8 Work out
   a) $\frac{1}{4} + \frac{1}{4}$ **b)** $\frac{3}{8} + 1\frac{1}{4}$ **c)** $2\frac{1}{8} + 1\frac{1}{4}$ **d)** $1\frac{3}{4} + 1\frac{5}{8}$ **e)** $2\frac{5}{8} + \frac{7}{8}$
   f) $\frac{5}{8} - \frac{1}{2}$ **g)** $3\frac{1}{2} - 1\frac{3}{8}$ **h)** $2\frac{1}{4} - 1\frac{5}{8}$ **i)** $3\frac{1}{8} - 2\frac{1}{4}$ **j)** $3\frac{5}{8} - \frac{3}{4}$

ACTIVITY 1

Feeler gauges are thin slivers of metal which are used to measure thin gaps. Fred has gauges of thickness $\frac{1}{16}$, $\frac{1}{8}$, $\frac{1}{4}$ and $\frac{1}{2}$ inches. Show how he can combine these to get every fraction (sixteenths) from $\frac{1}{16}$ to $\frac{15}{16}$. What will he need to get 1 inch?

Key ideas

- To change fractions to equivalent fractions, multiply or divide both top and bottom by the same number.
- To add and subtract fractions, first change the fractions so that they have the same bottom number. Then add the tops and leave the bottoms the same.
- Remember that $\frac{1}{4} = \frac{2}{8}$, $\frac{1}{2} = \frac{2}{4} = \frac{4}{8}$ and $\frac{3}{4} = \frac{6}{8}$.

12 Basic probability

You have already seen how to find the probability from equally likely outcomes, but this knowledge now needs to be extended.

Exam tip

Probabilities can be written as fractions, decimals or percentages but not as ratios or odds.

Probabilities from experiments

Often it is impossible to work out probability from a set of equally likely outcomes.

For instance, there is no set of equally likely outcomes for the probability that it will rain on 1 June or even for the probability of getting a head when you toss a coin if that coin is biased (not fair).

For these you need to carry out an experiment or a survey, or look at past records.

It is important to make sure that

1 you carry out the experiment or survey in as fair a way as possible

2 you carry out the experiment enough times (or look at sufficient past records) for any freak results to even out.

For example, if you are tossing a coin which you think is unfair, you must toss it in as fair a way as possible and toss it enough times. Ten times would be nowhere near enough.

In these cases

$$\text{probability of event} = \frac{\text{number of trials that gave the event}}{\text{total number of trials}}$$

ACTIVITY 1

Throw a dice 100 times and record the number of sixes you get.

Work out the probability of getting a six. Compare your answer with some of your friends, results.

ACTIVITY 2

Throw two coins 10 times and record the number of times you get two heads in the same throw. Repeat the experiment another 10 times and record the number of times you get two heads in 20 throws. Keep on doing the experiment until you have thrown the coins 100 times.

Copy and complete this table. Use a calculator to work out the probability.

Number of throws	10	20	30	40	50	60	70	80	90	100
Times with 2 heads										
Probability										

EXAMPLE 1

Ghalib wanted to find out the probability that a car driving past his school was a red one. He recorded the colour of 200 cars passing the school. The results are shown in the table below.

Colour	Blue	Black	White	Red	Green	Other
Number of cars	58	24	25	38	21	34

There were 38 red cars out of 200. So the probability of a car being red is $\frac{38}{200}$.

It must be emphasised that in using experiments or past records the probability obtained is only an estimate. In Example 1 the probability of $\frac{38}{200}$ is an estimate and could even be rounded to $\frac{40}{200}$ or 0·2.

Probabilities that have been found from looking at equally likely outcomes are exact.

EXERCISE 12.1A

1   This table shows the results of a survey to find out which shops people used most often. Use the table to estimate the probability of a person shopping mostly at

 a) Tesco   **b)** Morrison's.

Tesco	Sainsbury's	Kwiksave	Somerfield	Safeway	Asda	Morrison's	Other	Total
52	38	16	27	42	34	18	23	250

2   The table shows a batsmen's scores in his last 100 innings. Use the table to estimate the probability that in his next innings the batsman will score

 a) 20 to 29   **b)** 100 or more.

0 to 9	10 to 19	20 to 29	30 to 39	40 to 49	50 to 59	100 or more
8	12	25	16	14	22	3

3   Susan has made a six-sided spinner with the sides numbered 1 to 6. To test it she spins it 300 times. Her results are shown in the table. Use the table to estimate the probability of getting

 a) a 1   **b)** a 6 with Susan's spinner.

1	2	3	4	5	6
43	81	52	31	21	72

4   Ben wants to find out the probability that it will rain on his birthday. He finds out that it has rained on two out of his last three birthdays. He says that this means that the probability that it will rain on his next birthday is $\frac{2}{3}$. Why is he almost certainly wrong?

5   Lisa has a bag containing thousands of red and white beads. She does not know how many of each there are. Describe carefully an experiment Lisa could carry out to find the probability of choosing a red bead.

EXERCISE 12.1B

1 Ashraf has carried out a survey in his school to find out what drinks the pupils had with their breakfast.

The results are shown in the table. Use this table to estimate the probability that a student in Ashraf's school had

a) coffee   **b)** milk

with their breakfast.

Tea	Coffee	Chocolate	Milk	Fruit juice	Other	Total
28	33	15	24	31	19	150

2 Gail and Saima play chess against each other regularly. The results of the last 30 games are shown in the table. Use this table to estimate the probability that the next game results in

a) a win for Gail   **b)** a draw.

Gail wins	Saima wins	Draw
18	9	3

3 John tosses three coins and records the number of heads he gets. He then repeats this experiment 200 times. The results are shown in the table. Use this table to estimate the probability of getting

a) 1 head   **b)** 3 heads

when three coins are tossed.

Number of heads	0	1	3	4
Number of times	23	72	79	26

4 Rosie wants to find the probability that a student at her school will choose various flavours of crisps. Describe carefully a survey which Rosie could carry out. Include in your answer an observation sheet which Rosie could use to record her answers.

5 Hamid tosses a coin five times and gets four tails. He says 'This coin is biased'. Is he likely to be correct, and why?

Comparing theoretical and experimental probability

theoretical probability of an event = <u>number of outcomes which give the event</u>
total number of outcomes

Sometimes experiments are used to check if a dice, spinner or coin is biased.
To do this you need to compare the theoretical probability with the experimental probability.

EXAMPLE 2

a) When a dice is thrown, what is the theoretical probability of getting a six?

b) Paul threw a dice 80 times and there were 12 sixes. Work out the experimental probability of getting a six.

c) Does this tell you if the dice is biased? Explain your answer.

a) Theoretical probability of a six = $\dfrac{\text{ways of getting a six}}{\text{total outcomes}} = \dfrac{1}{6} = 0.17$

b) Experimental probability = $\dfrac{\text{number of sixes}}{\text{number of throws}} = \dfrac{12}{80} = 0.15$

c) It is unlikely that the dice is biased as the two probabilities are close. To be more certain, a much larger number of throws would be needed.

It is very difficult to be sure that something is biased unless the theoretical and experimental probabilities are very different and a large number of experiments have been done.

EXERCISE 12.2A

1 A bag contains six blue balls, three red balls and one green ball. One ball is chosen from the bag. Work out the theoretical probability of choosing a red ball.

2 When a dice is thrown what is the theoretical probability of getting
  a) a four   **b)** a number bigger than four?

3 Assume that people are equally likely to be born on any day of the week.
  a) What is the theoretical probability that a person chosen at random is born on a Monday?
  b) Mavis found out from 30 of her friends on which day they were born.
    Eight were born on a Monday. What is the experimental probability of being born on a Monday?
  c) She said that this proved that all days were not equally likely. Comment on her statement.

4 Kim tossed a coin ten times and it came down heads eight times. He said it proved the coin was biased.
  a) Find **(i)** the theoretical probability of a head
          (ii) the experimental probability of a head.
  b) Explain why his comment may have been wrong.

5 Solomon has a spinner in the shape of a pentagon. The sides are labelled 1, 2, 3, 4, 5.
  a) Work out the theoretical probability of scoring **(i)** 2   **(ii)** 4.
  He spun the spinner 500 times and his results are shown in the table.
  b) Work out the experimental probability of scoring **(i)** 2   **(ii)** 4.
  c) Do the results suggest that the spinner is fair? Explain your answer.

Number on spinner	1	2	3	4	5
Number of times	102	103	98	96	101

EXERCISE 12.2B

1 When a dice is thrown, what is the theoretical probability of getting

   a) 4   **b)** an odd number?

2 A survey of the type of washing agent used by 500 households had the results shown in the table. Work out the experimental probability that a household chosen at random will use

   a) liquid   **b)** tablets.

Type of washing agent	Liquid	Powder	Tablet
Number of households	220	175	105

3 Avril threw a dice 40 times and it came down 'six' four times. She said this proved the dice was biased.

   a) Find   **(i)** the theoretical probability of a 'six'

            (ii) the experimental probability of a 'six'.

   b) Explain why her comment may have been wrong.

4 Theresa did a survey on the colour of cars going down her road. These were her results. Find the experimental probability that the next car will be

   a) silver   **b)** blue.

Car colour	Black	White	Red	Silver	Blue	Other
Number of cars	16	25	19	28	8	4

5 George has a spinner in the shape of a pentagon. The sides are labelled 1, 2, 1, 3, 1.

   a) Work out the theoretical probability of scoring **(i)** 1   **(ii)** 2   **(iii)** 3.

   b) He spun the spinner 200 times and these are his results. Work out the experimental probability of scoring **(i)** 1   **(ii)** 2   **(iii)** 3.

   c) Compare the theoretical and experimental probability.

Number on spinner	1	2	3
Number of times	102	55	43

ACTIVITY 3

Now try this experiment to estimate how many there are in a population.

Put a number (unknown) of discs or counters in a bag. Place 10 (or so) of a different colour in the bag. Select a disc at random, note whether it is an original one or not, and return it to the bag. Mix the discs well and pick another one out. How many discs will you need to pick out before you can confidently predict the total number of discs in the bag? (This can be called 'How many fish in the sea?' This can also be repeated with cards from a pack [of an unknown number] of cards.)

Key ideas

- Probabilities can be given as fractions, decimals or percentages.
- Probabilities can be found by
  a) looking at equally likely outcomes (theoretical probability)
  b) carrying out a survey
  c) looking at past records
  d) carrying out an experiment.
- When there are equally likely outcomes,

  probability of an event = $\dfrac{\text{number of outcomes which give the event}}{\text{total number of outcomes}}$

- From surveys, past records, or experiments,

  estimated probability of an event = $\dfrac{\text{number of trials that gave the event}}{\text{total number of trials.}}$

Revision exercise

1 Look at this graph.

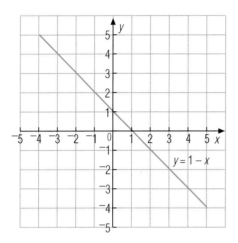

Find the value of *y* when

a) *x* = 4

b) *x* = ⁻2.

2 Look at this bar chart.

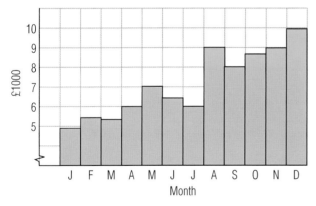

a) What were the sales in August?

b) Why is the chart misleading?

3 This distance–time graph show Petra's bike journey from Ford and back.

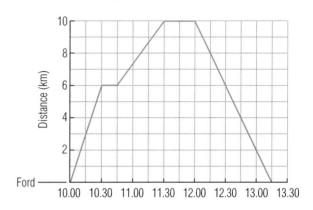

Answer these questions from the graph.

a) How far did she ride altogether?

b) How long did she rest altogether on the journey?

c) How far was she from Ford at 12.30?

d) At what time did she arrive back at Ford?

e) What was her speed on the first part of the journey?

4 a) Write down all the factors of

    (i) 10   **(ii)** 15.

b) Write down the common factors of 10 and 15.

5 Look at these numbers
    2   3   6   8   9   10   12.

Write down the ones that are

a) even numbers   **b)** factors of 24

c) multiples of 3   **d)** multiples of 6.

6 Work out

    a) $\frac{1}{8} + \frac{5}{8}$ **b)** $\frac{3}{8} + \frac{1}{8}$

    c) $\frac{1}{8} + \frac{1}{4}$ **d)** $\frac{3}{4} + \frac{1}{2}$

    e) $1\frac{5}{8} + \frac{1}{2}$

7 Work out

    a) $\frac{5}{8} - \frac{3}{8}$ **b)** $\frac{3}{4} - \frac{3}{8}$

    c) $4\frac{3}{8} - 2\frac{1}{4}$ **d)** $1\frac{1}{2} - \frac{1}{8}$

    e) $2\frac{3}{8} - \frac{1}{2}$

8 Jane carries out a survey to see how the students at her school travel to school. The results are in the table below.

Car	Walks	Cycle	Bus	Train	Total
41	47	33	62	17	200

Use the table to estimate the probability that a student in Jane's school travels by

a) bus   **b)** cycle.

9 Probabilities can be found using one of four methods.

    1 looking at equally likely outcomes

    2 carrying out a survey

    3 looking at past records

    4 carrying out an experiment.

Which of these methods would you use to find these probabilities?

a) The probability of getting a red card when you cut a pack of cards.

b) The probability of getting a head when you toss a biased coin.

c) The probability of a 17-year-old newly qualified driver having an accident.

10 A letter is chosen at random from the word PROBABILITY. What is the probability it is

a) a B

b) an L?

13 *Simple reflections*

You should already know

● how to plot and read points in all four quadrants
● the names and shapes of a square, a rectangle, a parallelogram, an isosceles triangle and an equilateral triangle
● the meanings of the terms right angle, acute angle, obtuse angle, reflex angle, horizontal and vertical.

Reflection symmetry

ACTIVITY 1

Making ink devils

Take a piece of paper and fold it. Open it and put a small amount of ink or paint in the middle, refold it, open it and look at the shape made. The shape will have a line of symmetry where you folded it. Here is an example.

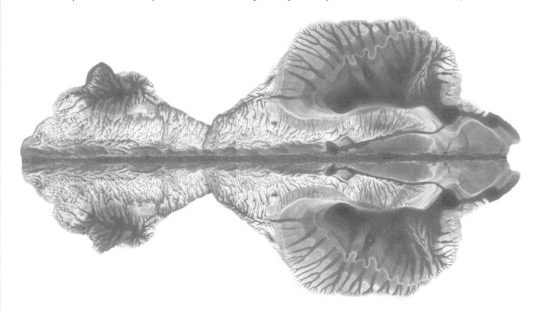

Try it again with another piece of paper.

Look at this picture of a house.

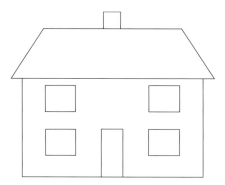

What do you notice?

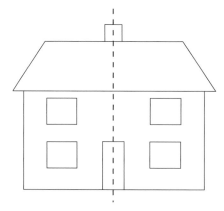

If you have a mirror, place it vertically along the dotted line. You should still see the house exactly as it was before.

Alternatively, make a tracing of the house and the dotted line. Turn the tracing over and place it back on the house so that the dotted lines are in the same place. It should fit exactly.

Shapes for which this works are called **symmetrical**.

The dotted line is called a **line of symmetry**. All the lengths and angles on one side of the line are exactly the same as the equivalent ones on the other side.

Some shapes have more than one line of symmetry.

Check with a mirror or tracing paper that both the dotted lines are lines of symmetry.

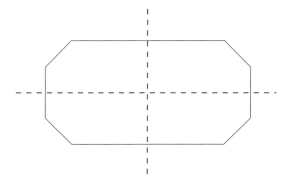

Check with tracing paper that the dotted line in the diagram below, is *not* a line of symmetry

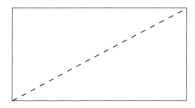

Exam tip

If you are not sure whether there is a line of symmetry, check using tracing paper. In examinations this is always available.

Completing shapes that have lines of symmetry

EXAMPLE 2

The dotted line is a line of symmetry for the given shape. Complete the drawing.

1 Trace the shape including the dotted line.

2 Turn the tracing over and lay it over the original so that the dotted lines are on top of each other.

3 Prick through the corners of the shape, using a pin or compass point.

4 Join up the pin pricks to complete the shape.

EXAMPLE 2

Both the dotted lines are lines of symmetry. Complete the shape.

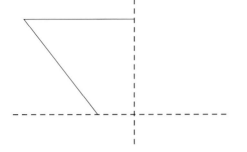

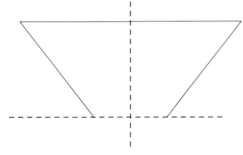

Do the same as in Example 1 for the vertical line of symmetry.

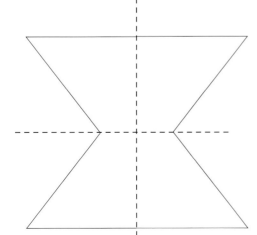

Now do the same for the horizontal line of symmetry. Remember to trace both left- and right-hand parts of the diagram.

Chapter 13 *Simple reflections*

EXERCISE 13.1A

Find all the lines of symmetry for the shapes in questions 1–6. When you have found them, draw the lines of symmetry on the worksheet. If there are no lines of symmetry, say so.

1 Rectangle

2 Square

3

4

5 Parallelogram

6

Exercise 13.1A cont'd

Use the worksheet to copy the given shapes and dotted lines of symmetry in questions 7–10. Complete the shapes.

7

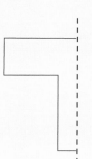

8

9

10

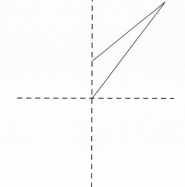

Chapter 13 *Simple reflections*

EXERCISE 13.1B

Find all the lines of symmetry for the shapes in questions 1–6. When you have found them, draw the lines of symmetry on the worksheet. If there are no lines of symmetry, say so.

1 Isosceles triangle

2 Equilateral triangle

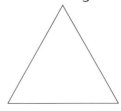

3

4

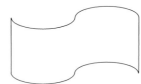

5

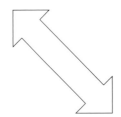

6

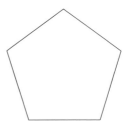

Exercise 13.1B cont'd

Use the worksheet to copy the given shapes and dotted lines of symmetry in questions 7–10. Complete the shapes.

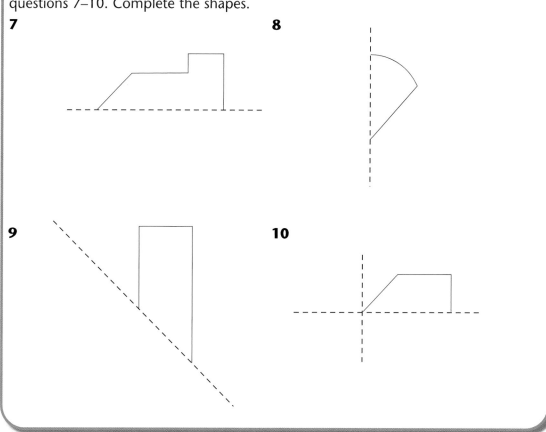

7

8

9

10

Rather than talking about reflective symmetry, sometimes you will just be asked to reflect a shape in a given line. When this is done, every point on the image will be at the same distance from the mirror line as it was on the object, but on the other side of the mirror line.

EXAMPLE 3

Reflect the shape in the dotted line AB.

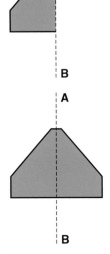

All the points of the image are at the same distance but on the opposite side of the line. The points on the line stay where they were.

EXAMPLE 4

a) Reflect the triangle A in the *y*-axis, and label the image B.

b) Reflect the triangle B in the *x*-axis, and label the image C.

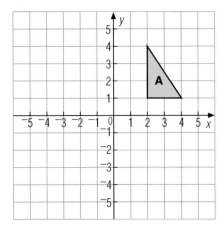

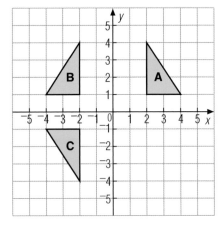

EXAMPLE 5

Reflect the trapezium in the line AB

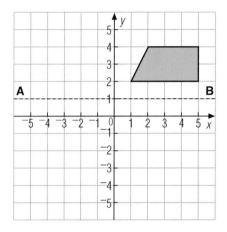

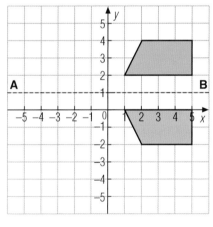

EXERCISE 13.2A

For questions 1–7 copy the diagram and carry out the reflection.

1 Reflect the shape in the line AB.

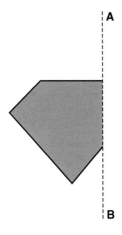

2 Reflect the shape in the line AB.

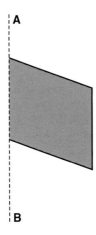

3 Reflect the shape in the line AB.

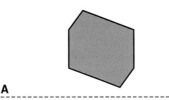

4 Reflect the parallelogram in the y-axis.

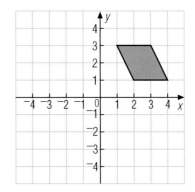

5 Reflect the triangle in the x-axis.

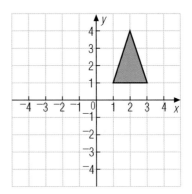

Exercise 13.2A cont'd

6 Reflect the rectangle in the line AB.

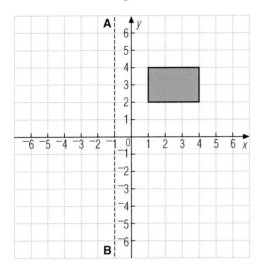

7 Reflect the triangle in the line AB.

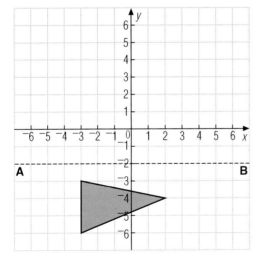

8 Draw axes from ⁻5 to +5 for both *x* and *y*.

a) Plot the points (1, 3), (3, 4), (1, 5) and join them to make a triangle. Label the triangle A.

b) Reflect the triangle A in the *x*-axis. Label the image B.

c) Reflect the triangle B in the *y*-axis. Label the image C.

d) Reflect the triangle C in the *x*-axis. Label the image D.

e) Describe the reflection that maps D onto A.

EXERCISE 13.2B

For questions 1–7 copy the diagram and carry out the reflection.

1 Reflect the shape in the line AB.

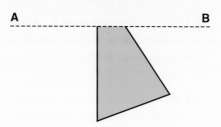

2 Reflect the shape in the line AB.

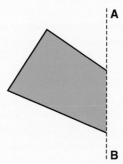

3 Reflect the shape in the line AB.

4 Reflect the shape in the y-axis.

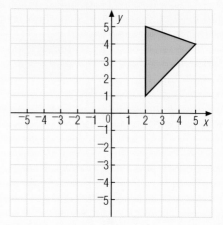

5 Reflect the shape in the x-axis.

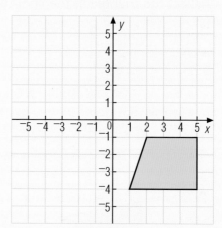

Exercise 13.2B cont'd

6 Reflect the pentagon in the line AB.

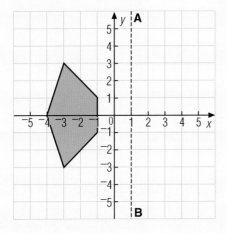

7 Reflect the quadrilateral in the line AB.

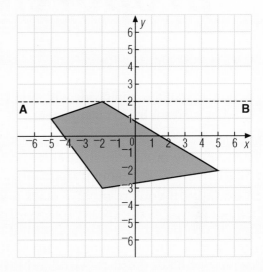

8 Draw axes from ⁻5 to +5 for both x and y.

a) Plot the points (0, 5), (4, 5), (5, 3), (1, 3) and join them to make a parallelogram.

Label the parallelogram A.

On the grid draw the horizontal line through $y = 1$ and label it PQ.

b) Reflect the parallelogram A in the y-axis. Label the image B.

c) Reflect the parallelogram B in the line PQ. Label the image C.

d) Reflect the parallelogram C in the y-axis. Label the image D.

e) Describe the reflection that maps D onto A.

Key ideas

● In all reflections, every point on the object is reflected to a point an equal distance the other side of the mirror line.

● If a mirror is placed along a line on a diagram and the shape still looks the same, then the mirror line is a line of reflective symmetry.

14 Ratio and proportion

You should already know

- how to multiply and divide with and without a calculator
- what is meant by an enlargement.

When you are mixing quantities it is often important to keep the amounts of ingredients in the same proportion.

For example, if you are mixing black and white paint to make a certain shade of grey, it is important to keep the proportions of black and white the same. If you mix 1 litre of black with 2 of white, then you would mix 2 litres of black with 4 litres of white, 3 litres of black with 6 of white and so on. The ratio of black paint to white paint is 1 part to 2 parts, or just 1 to 2.

Similarly, if two shapes are in proportion and the lengths of the larger one are all four times the lengths of the smaller one, you can say the ratio of the smaller to the larger is 1 to 4.

When a ratio is 1 to n

Multiply the first amount by n to get the second.

Divide the second amount by n to get the first.

EXAMPLE 1

A rectangle is 5 cm wide and 8 cm long. An enlargement of the rectangle is five times as big.

a) What is the ratio of the sides of the two rectangles?

b) What are the width and length of the enlargement?

a) The ratio of the side of the rectangle is 1 to 5.

b) Width of enlargement = $5 \times 5 = 25$ cm.

Length of enlargement = $8 \times 5 = 40$ cm.

> To find the size of the enlargement just multiply by the ratio.

EXAMPLE 2

The photos are in the ratio of 1 to 3.

a) What is the length of the larger one?

b) What is the width of the smaller one?

6 cm

12 cm

a) Length of larger photo = 6 × 3 = 18 cm.   **Finding the second, so multiply by 3.**

b) Width of smaller photo = 12 ÷ 3 = 4 cm.   **Finding the first, so divide by 3.**

EXAMPLE 3

To make orange squash, concentrated orange and water are mixed in the ratio 1 to 8.

a) How much water is mixed with 20 ml of concentrated orange?

b) How much concentrated orange is used with 400 ml of water?

a) Water = 20 × 8 = 160 ml.

b) Concentrated orange = 400 ÷ 8 = 50 ml.

Sometimes the ratios are given with different units. For example the size of the scale of a map can be given as a ratio of centimetres to metres, such as 1 cm to 2 km.

EXAMPLE 4

A map is drawn to a scale of 1 cm to 2 km.

a) The distance between Amhope and Didburn is 5·4 cm on the map. What is the real distance between them?

b) The length of the straight rail track between two stations is 7·8 km. How long is this track on the map?

a) Distance from Amhope to Didburn = 5·4 × 2 = 10·8 km

b) Length of track = 7·8 ÷ 2 = 3·9 cm.

Chapter 14 *Ratio and proportion*

EXERCISE 14.1A

Do not use a calculator in this exercise.

1 The ratio of the lengths of two similar triangles is 1 to 6.

   a) The length of the shortest side of the smaller triangle is 3 cm. What is the length of the shortest side of the larger one?

   b) The length of the longest side of the larger triangle is 30 cm. What is the length of the longest side of the smaller one?

2 The ratio of the number of helpers to the number of babies in a crèche must be 1 to 4.

   a) There are six helpers on a Tuesday. How many babies can they look after?

   b) There are 36 babies on a Thursday. How many helpers must there be?

3 Sanjay is mixing pink paint. To get the shade he wants he mixes red and white in the ratio 1 to 3.

   a) How much white paint should he mix with 2 litres of red paint?

   b) How much red paint should be mixed with 12 litres of white paint?

4 To make a solution of a chemical a chemist mixes 1 part chemical to 20 parts water.

   a) How much water should he mix with 30 ml of chemical?

   b) How much chemical should he mix with 2 litres (2000 ml) of water?

5 To make dressing for her lawn, Doreen mixes loam and sand in the ratio 1 to 3.

   a) How much sand does she need to mix with two buckets of loam?

   b) How much loam should she mix with 15 buckets of sand?

6 My road atlas of Great Britain is to a scale of 1 inch to 4 miles.

   a) On the map the distance from Forfar to Montrose is 7 inches. How many miles is it between the two towns?

   b) It is 40 miles from Newcastle to Middlesbrough. How far is this on the map?

7 The negative for a photograph is 35 mm long. A six times enlargement is made. How long will the enlargement be?

8 Sam mixes water and lemon curd to use in a cake recipe in the ratio 1 to 3.

   a) How much lemon curd would he mix with two tablespoons of water?

   b) How much water would he mix with 15 teaspoons of lemon curd?

EXERCISE 14.1B

You can use a calculator in this exercise if you wish.

1 Two rectangles are similar and in the ratio 1 to 2·5.

a) The smaller has a length of 5 cm. What is the length of the larger?

b) The larger has a width of 7·5 cm. What is the width of the smaller?

2 Mia mixes 1 part orange to 8 parts water to make orange squash.

a) How much water does she mix with 35 ml of orange?

b) How much orange does she mix with 336 ml of water?

3 The Michelin motoring atlas of France has a scale of 1 cm to 2 km.

a) On the map the distance between Metz and Nancy is 25 cm. How far is the actual distance between the two towns?

b) The actual distance between Caen and Falaise is 33 km. How far is it on the map?

4 To make mortar, Fred mixes 1 part cement with 5 parts sand.

a) How much sand does he mix with 500 g of cement?

b) How much cement does he mix with 4·5 kg (4500 g) of sand?

5

For a two stroke engine oil and petrol are mixed in the ratio 1 to 25.

a) How much petrol needs to be mixed with 2 litres of oil?

b) Jim put 16 litres (16 000 ml) of petrol in his tank. How much oil did he need?

6 An enlargement of a photo is 4·5 times the size of the photo.

a) The length of the photo is 4 cm. How long is the enlargement?

b) The width of the enlargement is 27 cm. How wide is the photo?

7 To make a shade of green, Ronnie mixes yellow and blue paint in the ratio 1 to 4.

a) How much blue paint must he mix with 500 ml of yellow paint?

b) How much yellow paint must he mix with 7 litres of blue paint?

Exercise 14.1A cont'd

8 The image from an overhead projector is 25 times the size of the drawing on the projector.

a) Richard drew a line 5 cm long on the projector. How large was it on the image?

b) A tree on the image was 165 cm high. How high was the drawing of the tree on the projector?

All the questions you have looked at so far have ratios of 1 to n but ratios can be n to m.

The examples are done by two methods. In the first method you find what 1 part is, and then multiply by however many parts are needed. In the second method you multiply by a fraction.

You can use either method, but be careful not to round any results until you get to the final answer.

EXAMPLE 4

To fill his plant pot, Terry uses 3 parts soil to 2 parts compost.

a) How much compost should he mix with 6 litres of soil?

b) How much soil should he mix with 8 litres of compost?

Here the ratio is 3 to 2.

Method 1

a) Soil is 3 parts, so 3 parts = 6 litres

$$1 \text{ part} = 6 \div 3 = 2 \text{ litres}$$

Compost is 2 parts = 2×2 litres = 4 litres.

b) Compost is 2 parts so 2 parts = 8 litres

$$1 \text{ part} = 8 \div 2 = 4 \text{ litres}$$

Soil is 3 parts = 3×4 litres = 12 litres.

Method 2

a) Compost = $6 \times \frac{2}{3} = 4$ litres

> **To find the compost from the soil multiply by 2 and divide by 3.**

b) Soil = $8 \times \frac{3}{2} = 12$ litres

> **To find the soil from the compost multiply by 3 and divide by 2.**

When a ratio is *n* to *m*

To find the second from the first amount, multiply the first amount by *m* and divide by *n*.

To find the first from the second amount, multiply the second amount by *n* and divide by *m*.

Exam tip

It is best to write down the ratio first – a useful check is that the bigger side of the ratio should get the bigger result. In Example 4a) compost is on the smaller side, and 6 litres of soil (bigger) are mixed with 4 litres of compost (smaller).

EXAMPLE 5

To make enough Yorkshire pudding for four people, Maureen uses 200 ml of milk. How much milk will she use for six people?

The ratio is 4 people to 6 people.

Method 1

4 people need 200 ml.

1 person needs 200 ÷ 4 = 50 ml

6 people need 50 × 6 = 300 ml.

Method 2

Milk for 6 people = $200 \times \frac{6}{4} = 300$ ml.

To find the amount for 6 people multiply by 6 and divide by 4.

EXAMPLE 6

Patrick has a recipe for celery soup for six people that uses 300 g of celery. He has 450 g of celery and plenty of all the other ingredients. If he uses all the celery, how many people can he make soup for?

Ratio is 300 to 450.

Method 1

300 g for 6 people

1 g for 6 ÷ 300 = 0·02

450 g for 450 × 0·02 = 9 people.

Method 2

He wants the second amount.

Number of people = $6 \times \frac{450}{300} = 9$.

EXERCISE 14.2A

1 To make pastry, Quentin mixes flour and fat in the ratio 8 parts of flour to 3 parts of fat.

   a) How much fat should he mix with 320 g of flour?

   b) How much flour should he mix with 180 g of fat?

2 In a recipe for Prawn Cocktail for 4 people 60 ml of mayonnaise, 60 ml of single cream, 10 ml of tomato puree and 200 g of prawns are needed. Fiona is making Prawn Cocktail for 6 people.

   a) How much single cream does she need?

   b) How many prawns does she need?

3 Jean and Terry agree to share their household costs in the ratio 2 to 3.

   a) Jean pays £20 towards food each week. How much does Terry pay?

   b) Terry pays £360 each month towards the mortgage. How much does Jean pay?

4 To make grey paint. Alan mixes 3 parts black paint with 4 parts white paint.

   a) How much white paint does he mix with 150 ml of black paint?

   b) How much black paint does he mix with 1 litre (1000 ml) of white paint?

5 A recipe for Raspberry Coulis for four people uses 250 g of raspberries.

   How many grams would you need for 10 people?

6 To make jam, Sanjay mixes sugar and fruit in the ratio 3 parts sugar to 2 parts fruit.

   a) How much fruit should he mix with 450 g of sugar?

   b) How much sugar should he mix with 800 g of fruit?

7 Claire mixes 3 parts of the chemical to 100 parts of water.

   a) How much water will she mix with 45 ml of the chemical?

   b) How much chemical will she mix in 8000 ml of water?

8 An alloy is made by mixing 2 parts of silver with 5 parts of nickel.

   a) How much nickel must be mixed with 60 g of silver?

   b) How much silver must be mixed with 120 g of nickel?

9 A recipe for Lentil Soup for four people uses 250 g of lentils, 250 g of carrots and 450 g of leeks.

   a) To make enough soup for five people, how many grams of lentils are needed?

   b) To make enough soup for nine people, how many grams of leeks are needed?

10 Jasbir is making mortar using 2 parts of cement to 5 parts of sand.

   a) How much sand does she need to mix with 1 kg (1000 g) of cement?

   b) How much cement does she mix with 1.5 kg (1500 g) of sand?

EXERCISE 14.2B

1 In a recipe for Haddock and Watercress Soufflé for four people, 400 g of smoked haddock is used. How much haddock would be needed for the recipe for seven people?

2 Brian and Joseph invest in a business in the ratio 2 to 3.

If Brian invests £3000, how much does Joseph invest?

3 Jason mixed 3 parts red paint with 5 parts white paint to make pink paint.

a) To make this paint, how much white paint must he mix with 750 ml of red paint?

b) To make this paint, how much red paint must he mix with 800 ml of white paint?

4 To make Spinach Soup for six people, 750 g of spinach leaves are used.

a) How many grams of spinach leaves are needed for soup for five people?

b) Janet has 500 g of spinach leaves. How many people could she make soup for?

5 To make jam, Ann mixes sugar and fruit in the ratio 5 parts sugar to 3 parts fruit.

a) How much fruit should he mix with 450 g of sugar?

b) How much sugar should he mix with 750 g of fruit?

6 Arun made a fruit punch by mixing 4 parts of orange to 5 parts of grapefruit to 2 parts of lime.

a) How much grapefruit did he mix with 500 ml of orange?

b) How much lime would he mix with 750 ml of grapefruit?

7 Mabel and Louise are given spending money in the ratio of their ages. Mabel is 4 and Louise is 9.

a) Mabel receives £2 in spending money. How much does Louise receive?

b) Louise gets an increase in her pocket money to £7.20. How much does Mabel now receive?

8 A metal alloy is made up from copper, iron and nickel, in the ratio 3 to 4 to 2.

a) How much iron is mixed with 75 g of copper?

b) How much copper is mixed with 120 g of nickel?

9 A recipe for Hotpot uses onions, carrots and stewing steak in the ratio by weight of 1 to 2 to 5.

a) How much steak is needed if 100 g of onions are used?

b) How many grams of carrots are used if 450 g of steak are used?

Exercise 14.2B cont'd

10 At Fairthorne School they had a sponsored swim. The money raised was shared between the school, the local hospice and a children's charity, in the ratio 2 to 5 to 9. The charity received £186.30.

   a) How much did the local hospice receive?

   b) How much did the school receive?

Key ideas

● When the amounts of two items are in the ratio n to m, use either Method 1 or Method 2.

● Method 1

   To find the second amount from the first, divide the first amount by n to find what 1 part is equal to and then multiply by m.

   To find the first amount from the second, divide the second amount by m to find what 1 part is equal to and then multiply by n.

● Method 2

   Fo find the second amount from the first, multiply the first amount by $\frac{m}{n}$.

   To find the first amount from the second multiply the second amount by $\frac{n}{m}$.

Rotational symmetry

You should already know

● how to describe line symmetry.

Look at this shape.

Check with tracing paper that there are no lines of symmetry.

Trace the shape. Place a pencil point or compass at O and rotate the tracing. You should find that there are three positions (the original plus two more) where the tracing fits onto the original drawing.

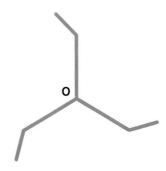

We say that the drawing has **rotational symmetry of order 3** about the centre of O. The order of rotational symmetry is the number of positions where the diagram looks the same as the original.

EXAMPLE 1

Describe all the symmetries for this shape.

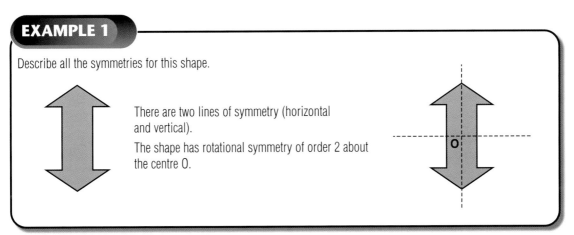

There are two lines of symmetry (horizontal and vertical).

The shape has rotational symmetry of order 2 about the centre O.

EXAMPLE 2

Describe all the symmetries for this shape.

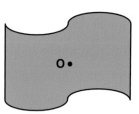

There are no lines of symmetry but there is rotational symmetry of order 2 about the centre O.

EXERCISE 15.1A

1 Describe the rotational symmetry of these letters.

a) H   **b)** A   **c)** N

2 Describe the rotational symmetry of

a) a square   **b)** an equilateral triangle

c) θ **d)** Φ **e)** $\mathbb{N}$

EXERCISE 15.1B

1 Describe the rotational symmetry of these letters.

a) S   **b)** B   **c)** X

2 Describe the rotational symmetry of

a) a rectangle   **b)** an isosceles triangle

c) $\emptyset$ **d)** ✳   **e)** ♣

Exercises 15.2A and 15.2B test both the rotational and reflective symmetry of shapes.

EXERCISE 15.2A

Use the worksheet or copy the following shapes. Draw in any lines of reflective symmetry. If there is rotational symmetry, show the centre and state the order of rotational symmetry. If there is no symmetry, say so.

1 Parallelogram

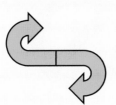

2

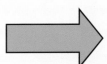

3

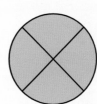

4

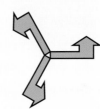

5

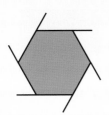

6

7

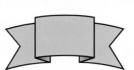

8

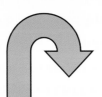

9

10

EXERCISE 15.2B

Use the worksheet or copy the following shapes. Draw in any lines of reflective symmetry. If there is rotational symmetry, show the centre and state the order of rotational symmetry. If there is no symmetry, say so

1

2

3

4

5

6

7

8

9

10 Circle

Chapter 15 *Rotational symmetry*

Key ideas

- If a shape looks the same in certain positions when it is rotated about a point, the shape has rotational symmetry about that point.
- The number of positions in which it looks the same is called the order of symmetry.
- The order of symmetry can be tested by using tracing paper.

16 *Solving problems*

You should already know

- how to add, subtract, multiply and divide, with and without a calculator
- how to find the square, the cube, the square root and the cube root of a number
- what odd, even and consecutive numbers are
- how to find the area and perimeter of simple shapes.

Sometimes you will be given problems to solve for which there is no straightforward method.

Look at the problem in Example 1.

This is a fairly simple example and you may be able to spot the answer. If you can't, then you need to find a method.

In this chapter two methods are going to be considered.

One method is **trial and improvement**. This is used in Examples 1–5.

EXAMPLE 1

John thinks of a number, doubles it and adds 5. The result is 37. What is the number?

Make a guess. Obviously the number is less than 37.

First try 10. Doubling it gives 20, adding 5 gives 25, which is too small.

Try a bigger number.

Second try 20. Doubling it gives 40, adding 5 gives 45, which is too big.

Try a smaller number.

Third try 15. Doubling it gives 30, adding 5 gives 35, which is just too small.

Fourth try 16. Doubling it gives 32, adding 5 gives 37. Correct.

The number was 16.

Try	Double	Add 5	Result
10	20	+ 5 = 25	Small, try bigger
20	40	+ 5 = 45	Big, try between 10 and 20
15	30	+ 5 = 35	Small, try between 15 and 20
16	32	+ 5 = 37	Correct

It is easier if you put the problem and working in a table.

EXAMPLE 2

A whole number is multiplied by 8 and then 15 is added. The result is 359.

Find the number.

Try	× 8	Add 15	Result
30	240	+ 15 = 255	Small, try bigger
50	400	+ 15 = 415	Big, try between 30 and 50
40	320	+ 15 = 335	Small, try between 40 and 50
45	360	+ 15 = 375	Big, try between 40 and 45
43	344	+ 15 = 359	Correct

Make a table.

The answer is 43.

Example 2 took five tries, and you might find it easier to use a calculator.

EXAMPLE 3

When a number is squared and 3 times the number is added the result is 154.

Find the number.

Try	Square	Add 3 times number	Result
20	400	+ 60 = 460	Big, try smaller
10	100	+ 30 = 130	Small but nearly correct, try a bit bigger than 10
11	121	+ 33 = 154	Correct

The answer is 11.

Example 3 only took three tries. Sometimes it might take more but, with practice, you should be able to find the answer in a few tries.

Each of these examples had only two steps, but you could have problems with three or more.

EXAMPLE 4

A whole number is multiplied by 6, 8 is then subtracted from it and the answer is halved. The result is 65. Find the number.

Try	× 6	Subtract 8	÷ 2	Result
10	60	− 8 = 52	÷ 2 = 26	Small, try bigger
20	120	− 8 = 112	÷ 2 = 56	Small, try bigger
25	150	− 8 = 142	÷ 2 = 71	Big, try between 20 and 25
23	138	− 8 = 130	÷ 2 = 65	Correct

The answer is 23.

EXAMPLE 5

Joe is twice as old as Maria and their ages multiply to give 1922.
What are their ages?

Joe's age	Maria's age	Product of ages	Result
40	20	800	Small, try bigger
60	30	1800	Small, try bigger
64	32	2048	Big, try between 60 and 64
62	31	1922	Correct

Joe is 62 and Maria is 31.

You know that Joe is twice as old as Maria so start with a try at their ages.

Remember that 'product' means the result of multiplying.

Exam tip
The order in which you do the operations matters – at each step work out the result before doing the next step.

EXERCISE 16.1A

Use trial and improvement to solve these problems.

1 A number is multiplied by 2 and then 6 is added. The result is 84.

Find the number.

2 A number is divided by 2 and then 3 is subtracted. The result is 87.

Find the number.

3 Bert thinks of a number, adds 7 and then multiplies the result by 6. The result is 336.

Find the number.

4 A number is multiplied by 5 and then 47 is subtracted. The result is 428. Find the number.

5 A number is cubed and 7 is subtracted. The result is 118. Find the number.

6 A number is squared and then twice the number is subtracted. The result is 255.

Find the number.

7 A number is multiplied by 4, 16 is added and then the result is divided by 2.

The result is 96. Find the number.

8 A number is squared, then 36 is subtracted, then this result is divided by 4. The result is 72.

Find the number.

9 Two consecutive numbers have a product of 756. Find the numbers.

10 Pam is 5 years older than Luke. The sum of their ages is 63. Find their ages.

11 In Park School there are 28 more boys than girls. There are 616 students in the school.

Find the number of boys and the number of girls.

12 To enter Sunberry fairground, the child ticket is £3 less than the adult ticket. It costs £27 for an adult and threee children. How much does each ticket cost?

EXERCISE 16.1B

Use trial and improvement to solve these problems.

1 A number is multiplied by 3 and then 4 is added. The result is 82.
   Find the number.

2 A number is divided by 2 and then 8 is added. The result is 31.
   Find the number.

3 Karen thinks of a number, subtracts 8 and then multiplies the answer by 5. The result is 335. Find the number.

4 A number is multiplied by 9 and then 41 is added. The result is 428.
   Find the number.

5 Pablo thinks of a number. He subtracts 27 and then finds the square root of the number he now has. The result is 17. What number did he think of to start with?

6 A number is cubed and then three times the number is added. The result is 4964. Find the number.

7 A number is multiplied by 3, 12 is subtracted and then the answer is divided by 2. The result is 96. Find the number.

8 Drew multiplied her age by 3, subtracted 4, and then multiplied by 5. Her result was 115. What is her age?

9 Two numbers have a difference of 6, and they add up to 104. Find the numbers.

10 Constance and her daughter went shopping. Constance spent £15 more than her daughter. Together they spent £185. How much did each of them spend?

11 Ameer is six years older than Mark. The product of their ages is 247. What are their ages?

12 The length of a rectangle is 4 cm more than the width. The perimeter is 28 cm. Find the dimensions of the rectangle.

Some of the problems can be done by another method, using a **reverse flow chart**. These are the problems with just one unknown at the beginning. Look again at Example 1.

EXAMPLE 6

John thinks of a number, doubles it and adds 5. The result is 37.

What is the number?

Number $\longrightarrow$ [× 2] $\longrightarrow$ [+ 5] $\longrightarrow$ 37

If the flow chart is reversed, working from right to left, you get

16 $\longleftarrow$ [÷ 2] $\longleftarrow$ 32 $\longleftarrow$ [− 5] $\longleftarrow$ 37

The number is 16.

> A flow chart is drawn. This diagram shows the steps of the problem.

> Notice that in the reverse flow chart everything is reversed:
> + becomes − and × becomes ÷.

EXAMPLE 7

Example 7 is the same problem as Example 2.

A whole number is multiplied by 8 and then 15 is added. The result is 359.

Find the number.

Number $\longrightarrow$ [× 8] $\longrightarrow$ [+ 15] $\longrightarrow$ 359

43 $\longleftarrow$ [÷ 8] $\longleftarrow$ 344 $\longleftarrow$ [− 15] $\longleftarrow$ 359

The number is 43.

> This is the flow chart.

> Reverse the order and every operation, working from right to left.

Example 3 cannot be done by this method because the unknown number is used twice. First this number is squared, which is all right, but then 3 times the number is added, and this cannot be reversed.

Example 8 is a new problem that can be done by the reverse flow chart method.

EXAMPLE 8

A number is squared and then 24 is subtracted. The result is 705.
Find the number.

Number $\longrightarrow$ [square] $\longrightarrow$ [-24] $\longrightarrow$ 705

Reversing

27 $\longleftarrow$ [square root] $\longleftarrow$ 729 $\longleftarrow$ [$+24$] $\longleftarrow$ 705

The number is 27.

The problem in Example 4 can be done, as the number you want to find is only mentioned at the first step. Example 9 shows how the answer is reached.

EXAMPLE 9

A whole number is multiplied by 6, 8 is then subtracted from the result and the answer is halved. The final result is 65.
Find the number.

The flow chart is

Number $\longrightarrow$ [$\times 6$] $\longrightarrow$ [-8] $\longrightarrow$ [$\div 2$] $\longrightarrow$ 65

Reversing

23 $\longleftarrow$ [$\div 6$] $\longleftarrow$ 138 $\longleftarrow$ [$+8$] $\longleftarrow$ 130 $\longleftarrow$ [$\times 2$] $\longleftarrow$ 65

The number is 23.

EXERCISE 16.2A

Find these numbers by drawing the flow chart and reversing it. (Many are the same as in Exercise 16.1A and obviously the answers should be the same.)

1 A number is multiplied by 2 and then 6 is added. The result is 84. Find the number.

2 A number is divided by 2 and then 3 is subtracted. The result is 87. Find the number.

3 Bert thinks of a number, adds 7 and then multiplies the result by 6. The result is 336. Find the number.

4 A number is multiplied by 5 and then 47 is subtracted. The result is 428. Find the number.

Exercise 16.2A cont'd

5 A number is multiplied by 4, 16 is added and then the result is divided by 2. The result is 96. Find the number.

6 A number is halved, 7 is then subtracted and the result is multiplied by 5. The final result is 55. Find the number.

7 A number is squared and then 30 is added. The result is 255. Find the number.

8 The square root of a number is found, then 14 is added and then the result is doubled. It comes to 46. Find the number.

9 To find the number of his house, Peter set his friends this problem. 'If I divide the number of my house by 9, multiply by 4, and then find the square root, the answer is 8. What is the number of my house?'

10 A number is divided by 3, 100 is subtracted and the result is then divided by 3 again. The answer is 9. What is the number?

EXERCISE 16.2B

Find these numbers by drawing the flow chart and reversing it. (Many are the same as in Exercise 16.1B and obviously the answers should be the same.)

1 A number is multiplied by 3 and then 4 is added. The result is 82. Find the number.

2 A number is divided by 2 and then 8 is added. The result is 31. Find the number.

3 Karen thinks of a number, subtracts 8 and then multiplies the answer by 5. The result is 335. Find the number.

4 A number is multiplied by 9 and then 41 is added. The result is 428. Find the number.

5 Pablo thinks of a number. He subtracts 27 and then finds the square root of the number he now has. The result is 17. What number did he think of to start with?

6 A number is multiplied by 3, 12 is subtracted and then the answer is divided by 2. The result is 96. Find the number.

7 Drew multiplied her age by 3, subtracted 4, and then multiplied by 5. Her result was 115. What is her age?

8 To find the approximate distance across a pond, Karen measured the distance round the pond, divided by 22 and multiplied by 7. Her answer was 17·5 m. What was the distance she measured?

Exercise 16.2B cont'd

9 Mrs Shepherd is quite old but she still likes puzzles. She set her grand-daughter this one. 'If you take my age, add 100, divide by 12 and subtract 5, you get your age.' Her grand-daughter is 11. How old is Mrs Shepherd?

10 A number is squared, 5 is subtracted, the answer is then multiplied by 6 and 11 is added. The result is 131. What is the number?

ACTIVITY 1

Use a calculator and trial and improvement to find the square root of the following numbers to 2 decimal places. (Do not use the square root key.)

40, 60, 80, 150, 250, 1000

Now use trial and improvement to find the cube root to 2 decimal places.

Key ideas

- To solve a problem by trial and improvement, try different values, deciding each time whether the answer should be more or less.
- To solve a problem by a reverse flow chart, set up the flow chart and then reverse the operations and the order of the operations.

Revision exercise

1 Copy these letters and draw any lines of symmetry on them. If there are none, write None underneath.

2 Describe the order of rotation of these shapes.

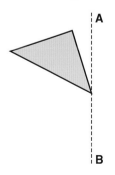

3 Copy this diagram on squared paper. Reflect the triangle in the line AB.

4 On a grid, draw axes from ⁻5 to +5 for both x and y.

a) Draw a dotted line vertically through $x = 1$. Label it PQ.

b) Plot the points (2, 2), (3, 4), (4, 4) and (4, 2) and join them to make a quadrilateral.

c) Reflect the quadrilateral in the line PQ.

5 The image on a screen from a slide projector is 50 times the size of the slide.

On the screen a man is 600 mm tall. How tall is he on the slide?

6 A recipe for Pancakes uses 4 ounces of plain flour and 300 ml of milk. This makes eight pancakes.

a) How much flour is needed to make 10 pancakes?

b) How much milk is needed to make 12 pancakes?

7 John thinks of a number, doubles it and adds 9.

a) Draw a flow chart to show the steps of the problem.

b) Reverse the flow chart and use it to find the number he started with when his result was 37.

8 Solve this problem by trial and improvement. Show your trials.

Basil was 27 when his son Brian was born. The product of their ages is now 688. How old is Brian?

INDEX

INDEX